SOIL SURVEY

TECHNICAL MONOGRAPH No. 6

SOIL SURVEY LABORATORY METHODS

Edited by
B. W. AVERY and C. L. BASCOMB

Contributions by
B. W. AVERY, C. L. BASCOMB, P. BULLOCK,
P. J. LOVELAND, P. D. SMITH,
and A. J. THOMASSON

HARPENDEN
1974

The Soil Survey of England and Wales is administered by the Lawes Agricultural Trust Committee, financed by the Ministry of Agriculture, Fisheries and Food with the advice of the Agricultural Research Council.

To be purchased from the Soil Survey,
Rothamsted Experimental Station, Harpenden, Herts.

Printed in England by Adlard & Son Ltd
Bartholomew Press, Dorking

CONTENTS

TEXT FIGURES

PLATES

TABLES

1 Introduction

B. W. Avery

This publication describes methods currently used in the Soil Survey of England and Wales to characterize soil materials in the laboratory. Most of the procedures are described in enough detail for them to be reproduced in other laboratories, but appropriate references are given to aid readers needing further information about the theory or technique of particular methods. Suppliers of special apparatus and materials are listed in the Appendix. Description and measurement of soil properties in the field, and procedures for collecting soil samples, are treated in the Soil Survey Field Handbook (Hodgson 1974).

Sampling units

The value of laboratory data in soil studies depends on effective sampling. Every sample should represent a definite body or class of soil that is as homogeneous as possible. The dimensions of the sampling unit depend on the purpose of the study and on the size of sample needed to obtain valid representation of the property determined. For example, if the proportion of stones is required, the sample must clearly be much larger than the largest stone present; otherwise the inclusion or exclusion of a single stone will affect the result significantly.

Samples of 1 g or smaller are sufficient for some analyses, and small but distinctive bodies of soil such as clay coats or mottles may be sampled as separate units in detailed pedological studies. For other purposes, samples may be taken from several sites to represent a much larger body of soil, such as the topsoil of a field or experimental plot, or that enclosed by a boundary on a soil map. The samples can be mixed for analysis, or analysed separately to characterize the body sampled in terms of the mean and variance of whichever parameters are determined. However, because of vertical and lateral variability, a very large number of analyses is needed to characterize many bodies of soil in this way.

Hence, in general soil surveys, mappable bodies of soil are characterized primarily by properties of the soil profile that can be measured or assessed in the field at numerous sampling points, using an appropriate classification (Avery 1973). Laboratory determinations are made on samples collected from selected 'bench-mark' soils to standardize and confirm field estimates of properties, such as particle-size distribution and organic-matter content, on which the classification is based, and to evaluate accessory properties not used for classification. For these purposes the basic sampling units are generally soil horizons, *i.e.* more or less homogeneous layers of soil delimited as elements of the soil profile at sites selected to represent a particular class of profiles, *e.g.* a soil series.

The Soil Survey of England and Wales uses undisturbed cores 15 cm in diameter extracted by a Proline soil coring machine (Plate I), or specially dug pits about 1·5 m long and 1 m wide, to identify and examine soil horizons at sampling sites. Horizon samples large enough for many laboratory determinations can usually be taken from Proline cores, but the shape and short-distance lateral variability of horizons, and important properties of individual horizons such as structure (pedality) and stone content, often cannot be assessed adequately. For this reason a pit is preferred when the objective is to characterize a soil profile as fully as possible.

Kinds of sample

Samples collected from soil horizons include (1) disturbed (fragmental or loose) samples for particle-size, chemical and mineralogical analyses; and (2) undisturbed samples for volumetric measurements and studies of moisture-release, structural and micromorphological characteristics. Undisturbed monoliths representing the whole soil profile are also taken, whenever possible with the Proline corer, for exhibition and comparative purposes.

Disturbed samples are normally air dried, screened through a 2 mm sieve, and subsampled for laboratory measurements, most of which are based on unit mass (weight) of oven-dry soil material < 2 mm, or of a smaller particle-size separate. However, the primary sampling units are volumes of soil, and interpretations of soil data are often more usefully expressed on a volume basis. As the mass of fine earth < 2 mm per unit volume can vary greatly, within profiles as well as laterally, the investigator needs to assess and record the contribution of all components of the soil to the total volume. This involves measuring or assessing the bulk density of the fine earth and the percentage by volume of stones coarser than 2 mm.

Stony soils

Very stony soils present serious sampling problems, partly because coring implements are ineffective, and partly because samples need to be large to get valid estimates of stone content. Ideally, samples for measuring stone content by volume or by weight should be 100 times larger than the largest size of stone present, as exemplified in the following Table.

TABLE 1

Minimum Sample Sizes for Estimating Stone Content

Effective diameter of largest particle *mm*	*Minimum volume of sample* *l*	*Minimum mass of sample (particle density 2·7)* *kg*
20	0·4	1·1
60	11	30
200	400	1000

Stone content is usually estimated by volume (or strictly by area) in the field by comparing the appearance of a vertical or horizontal face with figures illustrating various proportionate areas, or by superimposing a suitable grid and counting the number of grid intersections that fall on stones. For more accurate work, the stones in a sample of appropriate size can be separated by sieving and the proportion measured either by volume or by mass (Section 4.1.2). Percentages of a stone fraction by volume can be converted into percentages by mass and *vice-versa*, using the following formulae, where D_{bf} is the bulk density of the fine earth fraction and D_{bs} the bulk density of the stones (approximately 2·7 for most non-porous rocks).

$$\text{Mass }\% = \frac{D_{bs} \times \text{volume }\%}{D_{bf}(100 - \text{volume }\%) + D_{bs} \times \text{volume }\%} \times 100.$$

$$\text{Volume }\% = \frac{\text{mass }\% \times D_{bf}}{(100 - \text{mass }\%)D_{bs} + \text{mass }\% \times D_{bf}} \times 100.$$

Table 2 gives mass % equivalents of volume % estimates for stones of specific gravity 2·7 in fine earth of various bulk densities.

Proportions of very small (2–6 mm) and small (6–20 mm) stones are difficult to estimate by volume in the field, and can be determined in the laboratory (Section 2.1) if a large enough sample (*c.* 2 kg) is taken.

Precision and accuracy

In formulating analytical procedures and using the results, both the accuracy and the precision of the data have to be considered. If an analysis of a soil sample is repeated and the result is the same each time, the determination is said to have high *precision*. The *accuracy* of the data is its correctness relative to some absolute standard. For many conventional soil analyses there are no absolute standards. Different methods give differing results, and one method may give more useful results for certain purposes or on certain soils than another, but the greater correctness of the data remains unproven. Hence the method by which a soil property is measured should always be specified, and soils can only be compared rigorously if the same method is used.

TABLE 2

Mass % Equivalents of Volume % Estimates for Stones

(sp. gr. 2·7)

% *stones by volume*	*% stones by mass when the bulk density ($g\ cm^{-3}$) of the fine earth is*					
	0·5	*1·0*	*1·3*	*1·5*	*1·7*	*2·0*
5	22	12	10	9	8	7
10	38	23	19	17	15	13
15	49	32	27	25	22	19
20	57	40	34	31	28	25
25	64	47	41	38	34	31
30	70	54	47	44	40	37
35	74	59	53	50	46	42
40	78	64	58	55	51	47
45	82	69	63	60	56	52
50	84	73	68	64	61	57
55	87	77	72	69	66	62
60	89	80	76	73	70	67
65	91	83	80	77	75	71
70	93	86	83	81	79	76
75	94	89	86	84	83	80
80	96	92	89	88	86	84
85	97	94	92	91	90	88

References

AVERY, B. W. (1973). Soil classification in the Soil Survey of England and Wales. *J. Soil Sci.* **24,** 324–38.

HODGSON, J. M. (Ed.) (1974). *Soil Survey Field Handbook.* Tech. Monogr. Soil Surv. No. 5.

Plate I

Proline soil corer.

Plate IIa

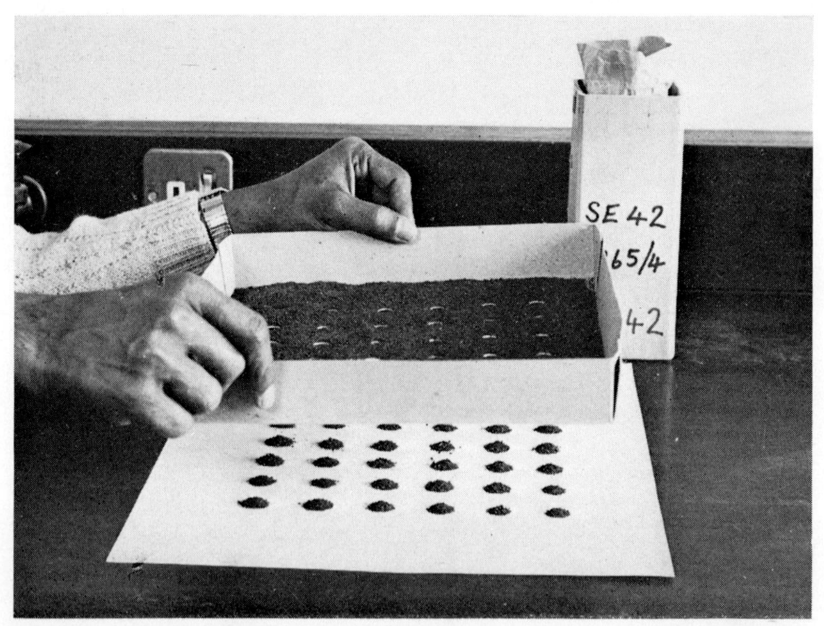

Subsampling tray.

Plate IIb

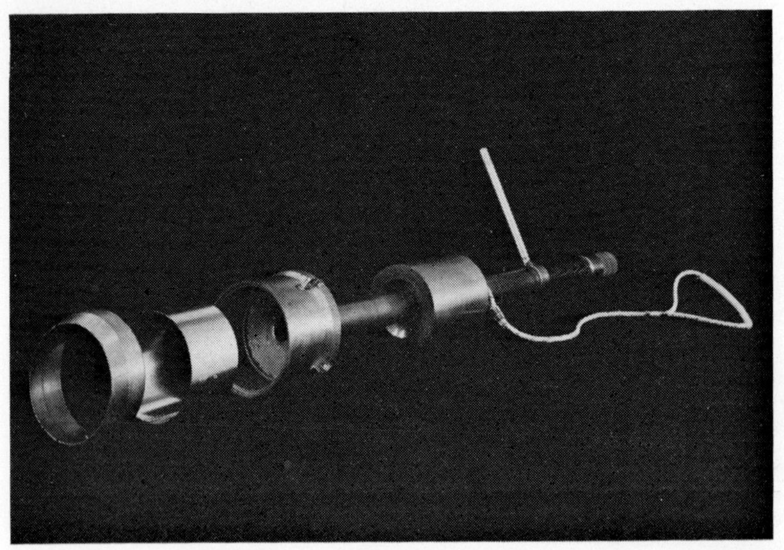

Coring device.

2 Sample Preparation and Stone Content

C. L. Bascomb and P. Bullock

2.1 AIR-DRY < 2 mm SAMPLES

2.1.1 Mineral soil ($<$ *c.* 30% organic matter)

Apparatus

Air drying cabinet maintained at 25–30°C, well ventilated
Sieves, 20 mm, 6 mm and 2 mm (B.S. 410)
Rukuhia soil crusher, 2 mm round hole screen (Waters and Sweetman 1955) (Appendix, p. 82)

Procedure

Spread the field sample on a drying tray, break down clods to about 3 cm and place in drying cabinet until air dry (24–48 hours).

If stone fractions < 20 mm are to be determined, record the mass (T) of air-dry sample. Hand sieve on 20 mm sieve and record mass ($S1$) of stones retained. When it is important to avoid comminution of soft rock fragments (*e.g.* chalk, shale), the < 20 mm sample must be hand-screened on a 2 mm sieve, gently breaking aggregates; *otherwise* transfer all material passing the 20 mm sieve to the drum of the Rukuhia soil crusher and revolve until all aggregated material has been reduced to < 2 mm and passed into collecting tray. Mix carefully and transfer to labelled box for storage. Remove from drum and place on 6 mm sieve. Record mass ($S2$) of 6–20 mm stones retained and mass ($S3$) of < 6 mm stones passed through.

If no determination of stone content is required, crush or hand-screen the air-dry sample as described above, without weighing, and discard material > 2 mm.

Calculations

$$\text{2–6 mm stones \%} = \frac{S3 \times 100}{T - S1}.$$

$$\text{6–20 mm stones \%} = \frac{S2 \times 100}{T - S1}.$$

References

British Standards Institution (1969). *Specification for test sieves.* B.S. 410.

Waters, D. F. and Sweetman, I. C. (1955). The Rukuhia soil grinder. *Soil Sci.* **79,** 411–13.

2.1.2 Peat soil (> *c.* 30% organic matter)

Apparatus

Air drying cabinet maintained at 25–30°C, well ventilated
Sieve, 2 mm (B.S. 410)

Procedure

Take about two-thirds of the moist sieved material (Section 2.2 below) and spread it on a drying tray. Place in drying cabinet. Stir once each day until air dry. Break up by hand and pass through a 2 mm sieve, discarding firm woody pieces and roots > 2 mm. Store in labelled container.

2.1.3 Subsampling

Apparatus

Subsampling tray* (Plate IIa)
Sieve, 500 μm (B.S. 410)
Morrice mechanical agate pestle and mortar
Glen Creston Hammer Mill with 0·5 mm screen

Procedure

Place the subsampling tray on a sheet of paper. Spread the < 2 mm air-dry soil in an even layer in the tray. Carefully lift the tray off the paper and return the remaining contents of the tray to the sample box. Collect the subsample from the paper. If it is still too large, repeat the procedure.

If carbon, nitrogen or calcium carbonate are to be determined in mineral soil, grind not less than 20 g of the subsample in the agate mortar to pass 500 μm sieve. If the soil is peat, mill 10 g of the subsample in the Glen Creston machine to pass 0·5 mm screen. Store in a labelled tube in the same box as the < 2 mm sample.

Reference

British Standards Institution (1969). *Specification for test sieves.* B.S. 410.

2.2 FIELD-MOIST PEAT SAMPLES

Apparatus

Sieve, 20 mm (B.S. 410)

Procedure

Samples are received in moisture-proof containers, *e.g.* sealed polythene bags. Each sample is gently hand sieved, using a 20 mm sieve and taking care that undecomposed plant structural units > 20 mm are not broken. The operation is done as quickly as possible to avoid loss of water. The sieved sample is returned to a moisture proof container.

* Designed by K. Thanigasalam.

The layer of peat in contact with a gas-permeable polythene bag may undergo oxidation during prolonged storage in the moist state and should therefore be avoided when abstracting subsamples for analysis.

2.3 THIN SECTIONS

Undisturbed samples for micromorphological studies are collected whenever possible in rectangular boxes, termed Kubiena boxes, made of brass or aluminium. They are hinged in one corner to facilitate removal of the sample and have lids at top and bottom. The size of box varies with the size of the section required, which in turn depends on the purpose for which the study is being made.

If the sample is intended to represent a soil horizon identified and described in the field, samples large enough to make a section 15 × 8 cm are preferable. Alternatively, triplicate randomly sited sections of smaller (7·5 × 2·5 cm) size, or composite sections (Grossman 1964) may be used. For purposive sampling, when specific macroscopic features are selected for characterization in detail, the size of the sample will depend on the size of the feature.

References

GROSSMAN, R. B. (1964). Composite thin sections for estimation of clay-film volume. *Proc. Soil Sci. Soc. Am.* **28,** 132–3.

HODGSON, J. M. (Ed.) (1974). *Soil Survey Field Handbook*. Tech. Monogr. Soil Surv. No. 5.

2.3.1 Impregnation of dried samples using Autoplax 110C

Apparatus

Air drying cabinet (Section 2.1)
Oven or freeze drier
Lightweight polythene boxes to fit samples
Mechanical stirrer
Vacuum desiccator
Resin reservoirs

Materials (Appendix, p. 82)

Autoplax resin 110C
Autoplax Styrene Monomer C
Catalyst powder 2
Accelerator 5
Uvitex OB fluorescent dye

Procedure

Preparation of samples. All samples must be dried because the polyester resin is immiscible with water. Samples with a small water-retention capacity are air dried in their containers for one week before impregnation. Those with a large water-retention capacity are freeze or oven dried, the former being recommended. If freeze dried, only the outer parts of the sample should be used for sections.

When dry, the samples are transferred to individual polythene boxes labelled with profile number, depth and orientation. Samples liable to collapse can either be left in the original sampling tin until after impregnation (which can spoil the tin for further sampling) or sprayed with a cellulose acetate solution until firm enough to be removed.

*Impregnation with Autoplax 110C**. Autoplax 110C is a polyester resin which on addition of catalyst and accelerator hardens a soil sample so that sections can be prepared using rock sectioning equipment. The addition of fluorescent dye to the impregnating mixture enables voids to be clearly seen in the finished section when viewed under u.v. light and thus aids their measurement. The composition of the impregnating resin mixture is in Column 2, Table 3. The Autoplax resin and Styrene Monomer C are mixed for 5 min with a mechanical stirrer. The catalyst and fluorescent dye are then added and the whole mechanically stirred again. A litre of impregnating mixture is sufficient for four containers with samples.

Individual containers with samples are placed on rotatable trays in a vacuum desiccator (Fig. 1) and evacuated for 15 min before addition of the impregnating mixture.

TABLE 3
Composition of Resin Mixture used in Thin Section Preparation

	Impregnation	*Replenishment*	*Re-impregnation*	*Fixing of section and cover slip*
Autoplax resin 110C	660 ml	660 ml	200 ml	25 ml
Styrene Monomer C	340 ml			
Accelerator 5			2–3 ml	0·5 g
Catalyst powder 2	4 g	4 g	6 g	1 g
Uvitex OB dye	4 g	2 g	0·5 g	

* Due to a current world shortage of styrene, a method based on Bakelite resin using acetone instead of styrene is being investigated as a possible replacement for Autoplax. Details of the Bakelite method can be obtained from FitzPatrick (1970), but it should be noted that the manufacturers have now replaced the resin BK 9001 by BK 9191, and this requires four times more catalyst than the original BK 9001.

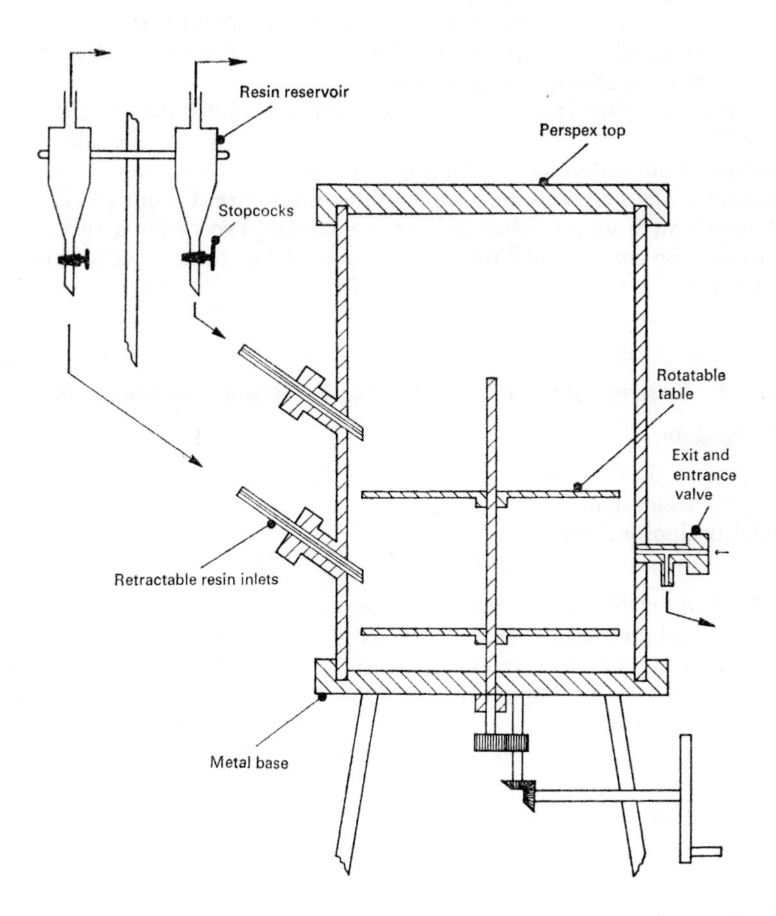

Fig. 1. Vacuum desiccator for impregnation with Autoplax 110C.

The resin mixture in two reservoirs above the desiccator is added to the evacuated samples individually by means of retractable inlet tubes and rotation of the table. When the resin has been added, the system is evacuated for a further 12 hours, at the end of which the vacuum is released slowly over a period of 5 min and the samples removed to a fume cupboard to polymerize.

Polymerization of impregnating mixture. Polymerization time can be adjusted by changing the amount of catalyst. Normally a period of at least 3 weeks, using the standard composition in Table 3, is advisable to reduce stresses and strains on gelling to a minimum.

During the early stages of gelling, the level of liquid in the containers falls due to evaporation of styrene. Samples must remain covered by liquid, otherwise air may re-enter. Thus the original level of the liquid should be regularly maintained using a replenishment mixture (Column 3, Table 3). After about 6 weeks, when gelling is complete except for a tacky outer surface, the samples are transferred to a drying oven at 40°C for final hardening.

2.3.2 Impregnation of moist samples using Carbowax 6000

Materials

Carbowax 6000
Crystal violet dye
1,1,1,trichloroethane

The use of Carbowax 6000 to impregnate moist samples of clays and organic soils has been demonstrated by Mitchell (1956), Morgenstern and Tchalenko (1967) and Greene-Kelly and Chapman (1970). It can also be used for soils containing as little as 20% clay. Because samples need not be dried first, shrinkage is reduced to a minimum and the method is therefore preferable to that using polyester resins when pore space is to be measured in thin sections. Its main disadvantage is that thin sections need to be mainly hand processed.

Procedure

Samples are immersed in a 10% aqueous solution of Carbowax for 5 min, followed by 2 hours in a 25% and 4 hours in a 50% aqueous solution. The temperature is then raised to 65°C and the sample left at this temperature overnight. The sample is then immersed in pure Carbowax which is changed twice during the impregnation period of 5 days. Fairly dry (pF 2–3) or loose samples can be placed directly in a 50% aqueous solution. When impregnation is complete the sample is removed and allowed to set after draining as completely as possible.

Cationic dyes such as crystal violet are useful for studying voids. The dye can be added during impregnation or used as a stain after grinding the section and before mounting the cover slip.

References

FitzPatrick, E. A. (1970). A technique for the preparation of large thin sections of soils and unconsolidated materials. In: *Micromorphological techniques and applications*. Tech. Monogr. Soil Survey No. 2.

Greene-Kelly, R. and Chapman, S. (1970). The preparation of thin sections of soils using polyethylene glycols. In: *Micromorphological techniques and applications*. Tech. Monogr. Soil Survey No. 2.

Mitchell, J. K. (1956). The fabric of natural clays and its relation to engineering properties. *Proc. Highw. Res. Bd*, **35,** 653–713.

Morgenstern, N. R. and Tchalenko, J. S. (1967). The optical determination of preferred orientation in clays and its application to the study of microstructure in consolidated kaolin. *Proc. R. Soc. A*, **300,** 218–34.

2.3.3 Cutting, mounting and grinding

Apparatus (Appendix, p. 82)
Woco 220 Diamond saw
Hacksaw
Glass microscope slides
Dawe ultrasonic cleaner
Slide press
Jones and Shipman Model 540VS surface grinding machine
Metaserv Universal Polisher with twin lapping wheels
Carborundum papers
Metaserv lapping cloths
Dialap Diamond Compound

Materials

Shell fusus A lubricant oil (Appendix, p. 82)
Paraffin
Beeswax

Procedure

Preparation of sections impregnated with Autoplax 110*C*. Three slices, 1 cm thick, are sawn from each block with a Diamond saw using Shell fusus A oil as lubricant. The slices are cut according to the features to be examined and the orientation required for the section. If impregnation of the sample is poor, slices should be re-impregnated with the appropriate mixture.

A well impregnated slice is fixed to a planed steel block of about its size with beeswax. The block is placed on the magnetic chuck of a Jones and Shipman vertical spindle surface grinding machine and the upper face of the slice ground smooth. The slice is then removed from the block and the smoothed face polished on a lapping wheel with diamond paste. After thorough ultrasonic cleaning with deodorized paraffin, the slice is ready for mounting.

Better adhesion of slice to microscope slide occurs if the face of the glass slide is frosted either by placing it on the magnetic chuck and grinding until the whole surface is frosted, or by grinding by hand on a glass plate with carborundum powder.

The polished side of the slice is mounted face downwards on the frosted face of a microscope slide of the desired size with an Autoplax mixture of the composition given in Column 5, Table 3. As soon as there is complete contact between slice and slide, the whole is placed under a press exerting a pressure of 4130 $N m^{-2}$, which is sufficient to remove all entrapped air bubbles.

If care is taken to use sets of slides of uniform thickness and to mount a polished face with a known pressure, it is possible to grind batches of sections to a uniform thickness. Sections are placed on the magnetic chuck of the surface grinding machine. Held in place by metal strips, they may be ground to a thickness of 40 μm or less. Usually 40 μm is sufficient as further polishing will take them to the normal 30 μm thickness.

Preparation of sections impregnated with Carbowax 6000. Small impregnated blocks (< 3 cm diam.) can be successfully sawn with a diamond saw using Shell fusus A oil as lubricant. Larger blocks must be sawn by hand with a hacksaw because heat generated during mechanical sawing causes smearing.

One surface of a slice is ground flat on a lapping wheel using 400 and 600 grade carborundum paper, and paraffin as lubricant. When flat, the surface is washed free of lubricant with 1,1,1,trichloroethane.

The slice is then attached to a previously ground glass slide with the Autoplax mixture shown in Column 5, Table 3. The section is ground to 30 μm on a lapping wheel using 220, 320, 400 and 600 grade carborundum paper.

Polishing. After grinding, all scratches and grinding marks must be removed. To achieve this, all sections are polished on a lapping wheel using fine carborundum paper followed by lapping cloths with various grades of diamond paste. During polishing the section should be examined regularly to judge thinness. If the section is 30 μm thick, quartz interference colours are of the first order, *i.e.* white, grey and pale yellow.

Mounting the cover glass. Before doing this the section must be cleaned fully. This is most efficiently done by immersing it in a beaker of paraffin in an ultrasonic cleaning tank for 2 min.

After the last trace of paraffin has been removed by warming gently (Autoplax impregnated slices) or by 1,1,1,trichloroethane (Carbowax impregnated slices), an Autoplax mixture of the same composition as that used in mounting the slices is spread over the face of the section and a cover slip lowered gradually over it. Sufficient pressure should be applied to remove all air bubbles. After the resin mixture has set, excess is cut from the edges with a scalpel, the section cleaned again and labelled with relevant particulars.

3 Physical and Chemical Analyses of <2mm Samples

C. L. Bascomb

Analytical grade reagents are used throughout unless otherwise stated.

3.1 WATER CONTENT AND LOSS ON IGNITION

3.1.1 Water content

The air-dry or field-moist water content is needed for conversion of the results of all determinations, made on air-dry or field-moist samples, to an oven-dry basis.

Procedure

About 5 g air-dry < 2 mm mineral soil or 10 g field-moist organic soil is weighed into a porcelain basin and placed in an oven at 105°C overnight. After cooling in a desiccator the basin and contents are reweighed.

Calculation

% Water content

$$= 100 \times \frac{\text{Mass of sample taken} - \text{Mass of oven-dry sample}}{\text{Mass of sample taken}}$$

(air-dry or field-moist basis).

3.1.2 Loss on ignition

Procedure

The basin and contents from water-content determination (Section 3.1.1) are placed in a furnace at 850°C for 30 min. After ignition the basin and contents are cooled in a desiccator and reweighed. If the soil is calcareous, 950°C for 2 hours may be necessary for complete decomposition of carbonates. Re-ignition to constant mass is used to check completion.

Calculations

Loss on ignition %

$$= 100 \times \frac{\text{Mass of oven-dry soil} - \text{Mass of ignited soil}}{\text{Mass of oven-dry soil}}.$$

Corrected loss on ignition % for calcareous soils = Loss on ignition % − (0·44 × $\%CaCO_3$*).

* Obtained by calcimeter (Section 3.5.1).

3.2 PARTICLE-SIZE ANALYSIS

3.2.1 Pipette method on < 2 mm mineral (peroxide-treated) soil

Apparatus

Shaking machine—end-over-end
Centrifuge (250 ml bottles at 2000 rpm)
Racking stand—for sampling pipette (Plate III) (Appendix, p. 82)
Sieve shaking machine
Sieves 600, 212, 63 μm phosphor bronze gauze (B.S. 410)
Stirrer, hand-plunger type to fit 500 ml cylinder

Reagents

H_2O_2, 27–30% (100 vol.) S.L.R.
Dispersing reagent: Dissolve 50 g sodium hexametaphosphate (Calgon flake) and 7 g Na_2CO_3 (anhydrous) in water and dilute to 1 litre.
$Al_2(SO_4)_3.16H_2O$, 6%
$BaCl_2.2H_2O$, M

Procedure

Transfer 10·000 g air-dry < 2 mm soil to a 600 ml tall beaker, add 10 ml H_2O_2 and observe the reaction for about 30 min. If it has been vigorous further treatments with 10 ml H_2O_2 are necessary until no reaction occurs —allow 30 minutes for each treatment. Finally leave to stand overnight.

Wash down sides of beaker and dilute to 40 ml. Heat on hotplate at 90°C for 1 hour, maintaining volume at not less than 25 ml by washing down. Allow to cool, transfer quantitatively to a 250 ml polypropylene bottle, add 150 ml water, shake and then centrifuge for 15 minutes at 2000 rpm.

If supernatant is clear test for SO_4. (Place a few ml of the supernatant in a test tube. Add $BaCl_2$ solution dropwise. White ppt indicates SO_4.) If SO_4 present draw off supernatant, shake up residue with 50 ml water for 5 minutes—retest. Repeat extraction until negative SO_4 test is achieved. If supernatant is turbid add 2 drops $Al_2(SO_4)_3$, centrifuge and decant.

Add by pipette to the residue 10 ml dispersing reagent, release soil cake from bottom of bottle. Make up to *c.* 150 ml and place on shaker overnight.

At this stage pipette 10 ml of dispersing reagent into a tared evaporating dish, evaporate and dry at 105°C, cool and weigh to obtain mass of residue R (see calculation).

Quantitatively transfer the contents of the bottle, through a 63 μm sieve in a funnel, to a 500 ml cylinder. Wash the residue thoroughly on the sieve with water. Transfer the sieve contents to a beaker, evaporate, dry at 105°C, cool and transfer on to a nest of sieves, 600, 212, and 63 μm with lid and receiver. Place on sieve shaking machine for 15 min. Transfer contents of each sieve to a weighed crucible, dry and weigh. Denote the masses of residues as *SS* (> 600 μm), *S* (600–212 μm) and *V* (212–63 μm) respectively.

Wash contents of the receiver into the measuring cylinder and dilute to 500 ml. Place in a room where temperature changes are slow and do not exceed 3°C over 8 hour sedimentation period. Radiant heat, causing convection, should be particularly avoided. Plate III shows the lay-out.

When equilibrium temperature has been reached use the hand stirrer for 30 s to thoroughly mix the contents, avoiding the introduction of air bubbles. Carefully withdraw the stirrer and take a 25 ml sampling pipette sample immediately at 15–20 cm depth. Drain pipette into a tared polypropylene dish and add two 5 ml rinsings of the pipette. Contents represent the < 63 μm fraction. Mix the contents of the cylinder again similarly. Allow to sediment, withdraw pipette sample from depth of 9 cm at appropriate time (Table 4). Evaporate and dry the contents of the two dishes and denote their masses, in g, as *A* and *C*, representing < 63 μm and < 2 μm fractions respectively.

TABLE 4

< 2 μm Sedimentation Times at 9 cm Depth

Temperature °C	*Time* *hours*	*minutes*
15	8	10
16	7	58
17	7	45
18	7	34
19	7	23
20	7	12
21	7	1
22	6	51
23	6	42
24	6	32
25	6	23

Calculations

Denote the oven-dry mass, in g, of peroxide-treated soil as M_p, which is equal to $20A + SS + S + V - R$.

Denote water content (Section 3.1.1) as W% (air-dry basis), then % loss by peroxide treatment $= 100 - W - 10 \times M_p$.

Percentages of particles having less than the given equivalent diameters, expressed on a peroxide-treated soil basis, are:

$$\% < 2\ \mu\text{m} = \frac{100(20C - R)}{M_p},$$

$$\% < 63\ \mu\text{m} = \frac{100(20A - R)}{M_p},$$

$$\% < 212\ \mu\text{m} = 100\left[1 - \frac{(SS + S)}{M_p}\right],$$

$$\% < 600\ \mu\text{m} = 100\left[1 - \frac{SS}{M_p}\right].$$

Sedimentation times for other particle sizes can be obtained from Nomograph I (Tanner and Jackson 1947).

References

British Standards Institute (1969). *Specification for test sieves.* B.S. 410.

Soil Conservation Service (1967). *Soil survey laboratory methods and procedures for collecting soil samples.* Soil Survey Investigations Report No. 1. U.S. Dept. of Agriculture.

Tanner, C. B. and Jackson, M. L. (1947). Nomographs of sedimentation times for soil particles under gravity or centrifugal acceleration. *Proc. Soil Sci. Soc. Am.* **12,** 60–65.

3.2.2 Pipette method on < 2 mm decalcified peroxide-treated soil

Apparatus

Stirring machine (low rpm)

Reagents

NH_4OH, sp. gr. 0·88
HCl, 2M approx.

Procedure

Transfer 10·000 air-dry < 2 mm soil to a 250 ml polypropylene centrifuge bottle, add 20 ml water, place a low rpm stirrer in the soil suspension and add 2M HCl dropwise until CO_2 evolution ceases. Several hours may be necessary if hard limestone is present. Excess of acid must be kept to a minimum throughout.

When solution of carbonates is complete neutralize the suspension by adding ammonia solution dropwise until sesquioxides are precipitated. Centrifuge at 2000 rpm for 15 minutes. Decant and discard supernatant liquid. Wash by shaking up the residue with 150 ml water. Centrifuge and decant again. Transfer residue to a 600 ml tall beaker and proceed with peroxide treatment and particle-size analysis as described above.

Calculations

(a) Percentages are obtained on a carbonate-free peroxide-treated soil basis, calculating as in Section 3.2.1.
(b) If results are required on a peroxide-treated soil basis then:

From Section 3.2.1 M_p = oven-dry mass of peroxide-treated soil.
From calculation Section 3.5.1 obtain $\%CaCO_3$ (< 2 mm soil basis) $= C_s$.

Then $\%CaCO_3$ (peroxide-treated soil basis) $= \dfrac{C_s \times 10}{M_p} = C_p$.

Percentages of particle-size fractions on peroxide treated soil basis are equal to percentages obtained in (a) above multiplied by $\dfrac{100 - C_p}{100}$.

3.2.3 Fine clay ($< 0{\cdot}2$ μm)

Apparatus

Centrifuge (250 ml bottles at 3600 rpm)
Sampling pipette, 25 ml

Procedure

Pour 200 ml of suspension remaining after < 2 μm sedimentation time (3.2.1 above) into 250 ml polypropylene bottle. Spin for 15 minutes at 3600 rpm. Take just up to requisite speed; bring down using brake until the last moment to prevent the reversing of the motor and consequent disturbance of liquid.

Take a 25 ml pipette sample at 7 cm below the surface and transfer into a tared polypropylene dish. Evaporate, dry and weigh.

Calculation

$\% < 0{\cdot}2$ μm clay (peroxide-treated soil basis) $= \dfrac{100(20D - R)}{M_p}$

where D = mass of residue, M_p and R as in Section 3.2.1,

3.2.4 Fibre content of peat soils

Apparatus

Sieve 212 μm (B.S. 410)

Reagents

Dispersing reagent: Dissolve 50 g sodium hexametaphosphate (Calgon flake) and 7 g Na_2CO_3 (anhydrous) in water and dilute to 1 litre.
HCl, 2%

Procedure

Transfer 10·0 g field-moist soil (as used for water content and loss on ignition determinations, Sections 3.1.1 and 3.1.2) to a 1 litre stoppered bottle. Add 40 ml dispersing reagent (Calgon) diluted to 200 ml. Leave to stand overnight. Shake by hand for 1 minute. Pour on to 212 μm sieve standing in a large funnel supported in the sink. Wash the material on the sieve with water flowing gently from a rubber tube. Do not use a strong jet. If carbonates are present transfer to beaker, treat with 2% HCl until effervesence ceases, return to sieve and wash until effluent is clear. Place a receiver under the funnel. Invert the sieve and wash contents through funnel into receiver. After allowing fibre to settle, pour off excess water. Transfer the fibre suspension to a tared polypropylene dish, and evaporate to dryness in an oven at 105°C. Transfer to a tared crucible and determine mass lost on ignition (F) as detailed in Section 3.1.2.

Calculations

% Dry matter (field-moist basis) $DM_f = 100 - \%$ water content (Section 3.1.1).
% Ash (oven-dry basis) $A_0 = 100 - \%$ corrected loss on ignition (Section 3.1.2).

$$\therefore \%\ \text{Ash (field-moist basis)}\ A_f = \frac{A_0 \times DM_f}{100}.$$

$$\%\ \text{Fibre} > 0{\cdot}2\ \text{mm (oven-dry, ash-free basis)} = \frac{1000F}{DM_f - A_f}.$$

3.3 CATION EXCHANGE PROPERTIES

3.3.1 Soil reaction (pH)

Apparatus

pH meter with protected pH probe (combined glass electrode and calomel half cells)

Reagents

Buffer solutions standardized at pH 4, 6, 9
Reference soil (air-dry < 2 mm) of known pH
$CaCl_2 . 6H_2O$, 0·125M

Procedure

Standardize the pH meter and confirm that there is adequate leakage of KCl from the probe, otherwise inaccurate readings may be obtained with soil suspensions despite satisfactory results on buffer solutions. This is done by placing the probe in dilute $AgNO_3$ solution and observing milky trail of AgCl.

(a) < 2 mm mineral soil, air dry

Two measurements are made with 1 : 2·5 w/v suspensions (1) in water (2) in 0·01M $CaCl_2$.

Transfer 10 g air-dry soil to a 50 ml polythene beaker. Add 25 ml distilled water from tilt pipette. Stir and leave to stand for 10 minutes. Stir again and introduce pH probe. Record reading (a) when it is stable. Add 2 ml 0·125M $CaCl_2$ by pipette, effective concentration being 0·01M $CaCl_2$. Stir and record reading (b) when it is stable. Check that standard soil is giving correct reading.

(b) Peat soil, field-moist

Recording is made in 0·01M $CaCl_2$ at 1 : 20 w/v suspension. The mass of moist soil equivalent to 2·5 g dry matter is

$$\frac{250\text{ g}}{100 - \%\text{ water content*}}.$$

Weigh this quantity of moist soil into a 100 ml graduated polypropylene beaker. Add 4 ml 0·125M $CaCl_2$ by pipette. Stir thoroughly, then add distilled water to bring the total volume of suspension to 50 ml. Stir again and leave to stand 15 minutes. Stir again, introduce pH probe and record steady reading.

References

SCHACHTSCHABEL, P. VON (1971). Methodenvergleich zur pH-Bestimmung von Böden. *Z. PflErnähr. Düng. Bodenk.* **130,** 37–43.

SCHOFIELD, R. K. and TAYLOR, A. W. (1955). Measurements of the activities of bases in soils. *J. Soil Sci.* **6,** 137–46.

3.3.2 Ammonium acetate extraction

Applicable to non-saline non-calcareous soils only.

* Water content, field-moist soil basis, obtained under Section 3.1.1.

Apparatus

Leaching tubes 18 cm long, 4 cm diam.

Reagent

NH_4OAc, N(pH 7·0): Dissolve 77·08 g NH_4OAc (special grade for soil analysis) in water, cool, dilute to 1 litre and adjust to pH 7·0 using HOAc or NH_4OH.

Procedure

Prepare leaching tube by pouring filter paper pulp on to perforated base plate, apply gentle suction and tamp down to form filter pad.

Weigh 15 g air-dry < 2 mm soil and mix with similar volume of coarse (2–4 mm) silica. Transfer on to filter pad in leaching tube. Invert 250 ml volumetric flask of neutral NH_4OAc into the tube and control rate of leaching, slow dropwise, with pinchcock on outlet. When supply flask is empty apply gentle pressure from a blow ball to top of leaching tube to free as much as possible of liquid from the soil.

Transfer the leachate to a 250 ml volumetric flask and make up to the mark with water.

3.3.3 Exchangeable calcium and magnesium

Apparatus

Perkin Elmer 290 spectrophotometer with three-slot Bolingburner, air/acetylene flame

Reagents

$Sr(NO_3)_2.4H_2O$, 10% solution

Standard solution: 1000 ppm Ca: dissolve 2·497 g dried $CaCO_3$ in 100 ml water and 10 ml HCl and dilute to 1 litre.

Standard solution: 1000 ppm Mg: dissolve 1 g Mg ribbon in 100 ml water and 10 ml HCl and dilute to 1 litre.

HCl, M

Procedure

Pipette an aliquot of the leachate (Section 3.3.2) into a volumetric flask so that the final solution will contain 0·2–5 ppm Ca and 0·02–0·5 ppm Mg (usually 2 ml/200 ml is a suitable dilution). Add $Sr(NO_3)_2$ solution so that the final solution will be 0·2% $Sr(NO_3)_2$. Add M HCl to give a final concentration of 0·02M HCl. Dilute to volume with water. Prepare standard Ca and Mg solutions containing 0, 1, 2, and 5 ppm Ca and 0, 0·2, 0·5 ppm Mg, each with the same final concentrations of NH_4OAc, $Sr(NO_3)_2$ and

HCl as in the diluted leachates. Read standards and leachates using spectrophotometer with fuel rich for Ca but stoichiometric for Mg. Plot graphs of scale reading against Ca and Mg content of standards. The calibration should be linear within the ranges given.

Calculation

me Ca/100 g air-dry soil = ppm Ca from graph × dilution × 0·08333.
me Mg/100 g air-dry soil = ppm Mg from graph × dilution × 0·13706.
Report on oven-dry basis (Section 3.1.1).

Reference

DAVID, D. J. (1960). The determination of exchangeable sodium, potassium, calcium and magnesium in soils by atomic-absorption spectrophotometry. *Analyst, Lond.* **85,** 495–503.

3.3.4 Exchangeable potassium

Apparatus

Eel Flame photometer

Reagent

Standard solution: 1000 ppm K: Dissolve 1·292 g KNO_3 in neutral N NH_4OAc solution and make up to 500 ml with the same solution. Dilute by 10 and by 100 with NH_4OAc solution to give 100 ppm and 10 ppm standards respectively.

Calibration

At 0–10 ppm range the calibration is linear. Calibration curves must be employed with 100 ppm and 1000 ppm standards.

Calculation

ppm K in 250 ml leachate × 0·0426 = me K/100 g air-dry soil.
Report on oven-dry basis (Section 3.1.1).

3.3.5 Exchangeable sodium

Apparatus

Eel flame photometer

Reagent

Standard solution: 500 ppm Na: Dissolve 0·924 g $NaNO_3$ in neutral N NH_4OAc to final volume of 500 ml. Dilute by 10 and by 100 with NH_4OAc to provide 500 ppm and 5 ppm standards respectively.

Calibration

At 0–5 ppm range the calibration is linear. Calibration curves must be employed with 50 and 500 ppm standards.

Calculation

ppm Na in 250 ml leachate × 0·0725 = me Na/100 g air-dry soil.
Report on oven-dry basis (Section 3.1.1).

Correction

Ca interferes with Na determination owing to leakage of Ca radiation through the Na filter.

Subtract 0·00544 × me Ca/100 g from the me Na/100 g calculated above.

3.3.6 Extractable acidity (pH 11 approx.)

Reagents

Distilled water through which a stream of air bubbles has been passed overnight to reduce dissolved CO_2 content
NH_4OH, 0·2N
H.CHO solution, 38–40%
$BaCl_2.2H_2O$, 1·25M (freshly prepared)
NaOH, 0·10N, rendered carbonate-free by adding 3 ml $BaCl_2$ solution and standardized
HCl, 0·10N, standardized
Indicator: Mix three parts 0·1% thymol blue with one part 0·1% cresol red (100 mg cresol red triturated with 4·3 ml 0·05N NaOH and diluted to 100 ml with water).
NH_4Cl, 0·1N

Procedure

Weigh 10 g air-dry < 2 mm soil into a 250 ml polythene screwcap bottle. Add 100 ml 0·2N NH_4OH and shake for 2 hours. (Use one drop of capryl alcohol to break froth if necessary.) While mixing add 16 ml formaldehyde solution and shake well. Add 80 ml $BaCl_2$ solution and shake occasionally for 30 minutes. Centrifuge at 2000 rpm for 15 minutes. Decant supernatant liquid into a 500 ml conical flask, add 10 drops of indicator and titrate with NaOH to blue end point. Then add a further 2 ml NaOH. Record final burette reading (A_s). Back titrate with HCl to rose-pink end point. Record burette reading (B_s). Make blank determination using 10 ml NH_4Cl solution instead of soil; record burette readings A_b and B_b.

Calculation

Blank ml = $A_b - B_b - 10$ ml.
me extractable acidity/100 g air-dry soil = $A_s - B_s$ − blank ml.
Report on oven-dry basis (Section 3.1.1).

Reference

Mados, L. (1943). Eine Schnellmethode zu serienweisen Bestimmung der Adsorptionsungesättigheit von Böden. *Bodenk. Pflrnähr.* **32,** 351–8.

3.3.7 Cation exchange capacity (pH 8·1)

Applicable to calcareous and non-calcareous non-saline soils, and to < 2 μm clay separates (Section 5.1.4).

Reagents

Triethanolamine (S.L.R.) solution: 90 ml diluted to 1 litre and pH adjusted to 8·1 by adding approx. 140 ml 2N HCl. Dilute to 2 litres, mix and protect from carbon dioxide during storage.
$BaCl_2$, approx. 2N (244 g/litre $BaCl_2.2H_2O$ S.L.R.)
Buffered $BaCl_2$ reagent: Mix equal volumes of the above solutions.
$MgSO_4$, 0·05N (6·2 g/litre $MgSO_4.7H_2O$)
NH_4OH, 2N approx. (140 ml/litre 30% w/w NH_3)
E.D.T.A. solution, 0·02N: 3·723 g/litre E.D.T.A. (disodium salt)
Indicator: Omega chrome black VS 0·1% (prepared daily)

Procedure

(a) < 2 mm soil

Weigh 5 g soil into a 250 ml polythene centrifuge bottle with tight stopper. Note mass in g of bottle plus soil (M_1). Treat calcareous soil with 100 ml buffered $BaCl_2$ reagent for 1 hour with occasional shaking. Centrifuge at 1500r pm (RCF* 415) for 15 minutes and discard supernatant liquid. For non-calcareous non-saline soils this first treatment may be omitted. Treat with a further 200 ml buffered reagent overnight, centrifuge and discard supernatant liquid. Add 200 ml water and shake to break up soil cake. Centrifuge and discard supernatant liquid. Weigh the bottle with contents (M_2). Pipette into the bottle 100 ml $MgSO_4$, shake the stoppered bottle at intervals over a 2 hour period. Centrifuge and decant the supernatant liquid into a stoppered flask. To a 5 ml aliquot of this solution add 6 drops of 2N NH_4OH and 2 drops freshly prepared indicator giving a purple colour. Titrate with standard E.D.T.A.; colour changes through

* Relative centrifugal force.

red to blue at end point (Titre A_1 ml). 5 ml aliquot of $MgSO_4$ is similarly titrated (Titre B ml).

Calculation

The soil titre (A_1) must be corrected for the effect of the volume of liquid retained by the centrifuged soil after the water wash thus:
Corrected titre (A_2) $= A_1(100 + M_2 - M_1)/100$ ml
then
C.E.C. of the air-dry soil $= 8(B - A_2)$ me/100 g.
If the C.E.C. exceeds 50 me/100 g the determination should be repeated using less soil and the calculation adjusted accordingly.
Report on oven-dry basis (Section 3.1.1).

(b) Clay separate $< 2\ \mu m$ (Section 5.1.4)

Weigh 0·500 g of oven-dried clay into a 50 ml polypropylene centrifuge tube. 25 ml aliquots of buffered barium chloride and water are used, and 20 ml of magnesium sulphate. 5 ml aliquots are titrated as above.

Calculation

$$\text{Corrected titration } A_2 = A_1 \left(\frac{20 + M_2 - M_1}{20}\right).$$

$$\text{C.E.C.} = (B - A_2) \times \frac{20}{5} \times 0{\cdot}02 \times \frac{100}{0{\cdot}5}$$

$$= 16(B - A_2).$$

Report on oven-dry basis.

Reference

BASCOMB, C. L. (1964). Rapid method for the determination of cation-exchange capacity of calcareous and non-calcareous soils. *J. Sci. Fd Agric.* **15,** 821–3.

3.4 CARBON AND NITROGEN

3.4.1 Organic carbon

< 2 mm soil, ground to 500 μm (Section 2.1.3. Subsampling).

Apparatus

Set of 500 ml conical flasks with ground glass (B34/35) neck fitted with reflux condenser
Thermostatically controlled hotplate to accommodate set of flasks and maintain 145°C

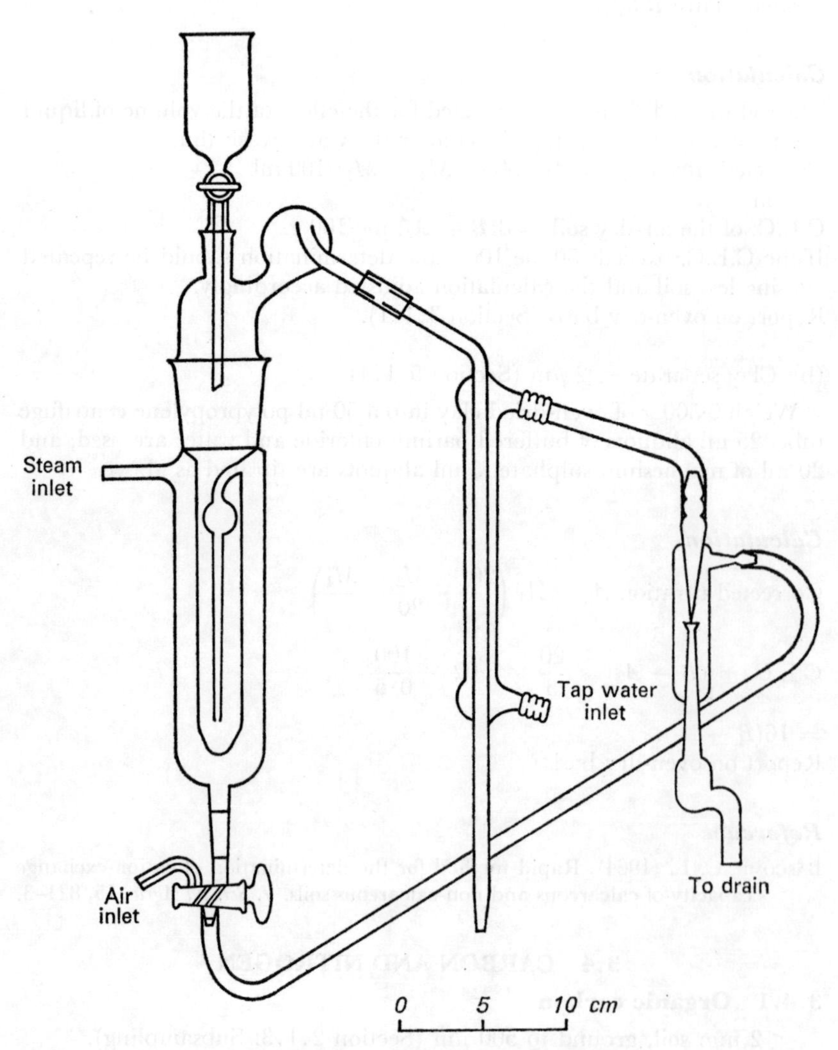

Fig. 2. Modified Hoskins apparatus.

Reagents

$K_2Cr_2O_7$ (dry), 0·2N: 9·8071 g/litre

$(NH_4)_2SO_4.FeSO_4.6H_2O$, 0·4N: Dissolve 314 g in 2 litres 0·75N H_2SO_4. Standardize daily by titrating against 20 ml 0·2N $K_2Cr_2O_7$ in the presence of 10 ml H_3PO_4, 50 ml water and 2–3 ml indicator—added last after mixing.

Digestion mixture: Dissolve 40 g $Na_2Cr_2O_7.2H_2O$ (S.L.R.) in 750 ml water. Cool and add slowly 800 ml conc. H_2SO_4 with thorough mixing. Cool and add 400 ml conc. H_3PO_4. Dilute to 2 litres.

Indicator: Dissolve 0·1 g barium diphenylamine *p*-sulphonate by warming in water. Add 10 g $BaCl_2$. Mix and dilute to 200 ml.

Procedure

A sample of < 0·5 mm soil containing < 18 mg C is weighed accurately into a 500 ml conical flask. 25 ml of digestion reagent is pipetted in and the mixture refluxed for 2 hours. Cool, add 100 ml water and titrate with $(NH_4)_2SO_4.FeSO_4$ (*AFS*) adding 2–3 ml indicator as the end point is approached. The colour change is from purple to green. The titre should be at least 10 ml; if not repeat the digestion using less soil.

With soil containing appreciable amounts of chloride, oxidation to chlorine can be avoided by use of digestion mixture containing 5% Ag_2SO_4.

A blank digestion is included with each set of determinations in order to assess the amount of thermal decomposition of $Na_2Cr_2O_7$ which has occurred.

Calculation

Organic carbon % (air-dry basis)

$$= 0{\cdot}30 \times \frac{(\text{ml } AFS \text{ blank} - \text{ml } AFS \text{ sample})}{\text{g sample}} \times \text{N of } AFS.$$

Report on oven-dry basis (Section 3.1.1).

Reference

TINSLEY, J. (1950). The determination of organic carbon in soils by dichromate mixtures. *Trans. 4th int. Congr. Soil Sci.* **1,** 161–4.

3.4.2 Pyrophosphate-extractable carbon

Apparatus

As described in Sections 3.4.1 and 3.6.1.

Procedure

A 20 ml aliquot of the extract is pipetted into a 500 ml conical flask (B34/35 neck) and placed in an oven at 80°C where it can evaporate to dryness without charring. Carbon is determined in the same flask as indicated in Section 3.4.1.

Reference

BASCOMB, C. L. (1968). Distribution of pyrophosphate-extractable iron and organic carbon in soils of various groups. *J. Soil Sci.* **19,** 251–268.

3.4.3 Total nitrogen

Apparatus

Kjeldahl digestion flasks, 100 ml, and heating rack
Hoskin's steam distillation apparatus, modified by addition of 2-way tap and filter pump (Fig. 2)

Reagents

H_2SO_4, nitrogen free
Salt mixture Kjeldahl Tablets (Fisons) containing 1 g Na_2SO_4 and 0·5 g Se
NaOH, about 45% solution
HCl, standardized 0·01N
H_3BO_3, 2% solution
Mixed indicator: Mix 0·1 g methyl red and 0·2 g brom-cresol green and dissolve in 250 ml ethanol; adjust to greyish mid-colour with dil. NaOH or HCl.
H_3BO_3/indicator mixture: Add 25 ml mixed indicator solution to 1 litre H_3BO_3 solution.

Procedure

Weigh 0·5–2 g soil (< 0·5 mm) into a 100 ml Kjeldahl flask. Add 3 g salt mixture tablets and rinse down the neck of the flask with just sufficient water to disperse the solids. Add from automatic pipette 10 ml conc. H_2SO_4. Heat gently on digestion rack in fume cupboard until any vigorous effervescence subsides, then gradually increase to full heat. More H_2SO_4 may be necessary if the mixture becomes viscous. Heat until a whitish colour is dominant, then continue heating for a further 30 minutes. Allow the flask to cool and then fill bulb of flask two-thirds full with water. Allow to stand with occasional shaking. Transfer the contents into a 250 ml volumetric flask and make up to volume. Prepare the steam distillation apparatus by passing steam through it for several minutes. Pipette a 20 ml aliquot of the soil extract into the tap funnel. Allow to run into inner chamber. Rinse the tap funnel. Add 5 ml of boric acid/indicator mixture to a 50 ml conical flask and place in position to receive the distillate, with the tip of the condenser just below the surface of the liquid. Add 5 ml 10N NaOH to the tap funnel (with the tap closed) and gently run it into the inner chamber. Follow this addition with two rinsings with water; throughout these additions always maintain a small amount of liquid above the tap to act as an air lock. Care is necessary to avoid contaminating the wash bottle with sodium hydroxide during the rinsing process. Collect 10 ml of distillate. Rinse the tip of the condenser, and titrate against 0·01N HCl, the colour changing from green through colourless to pale pink end point. Empty the inner chamber by turning the 2-way tap to vacuum and rinse chamber with water twice before reversing tap and introducing the next sample. Carry out blank distillation using 20 ml distilled water in place of digest.

Calculation

$$\% \text{ N (air-dry basis)} = \frac{(\text{ml HCl sample} - \text{ml HCl blank})}{\text{sample mass (g)}} \times 0{\cdot}175.$$

Report on oven-dry basis (Section 3.1.1).

References

HOSKINS, J. L. (1944). An interchangeable micro and macro steam distillation apparatus. *Analyst, Lond.* **69,** 271.

MA, T. S. and ZUAZAGA, G. (1942). Micro-kjeldahl determination of nitrogen. A new indicator and an improved rapid method. *Ind. Engng Chem. analyt. Edn,* **14,** 280–2.

3.5 CARBONATES AND SULPHATES

3.5.1 Calcium carbonate equivalent

(a) < 2 mm soil

Apparatus

Calcimeter (Fig. 3, Appendix, p. 82)
Barometer
The apparatus (Fig. 3) is described by Bascomb (1961). The reservoirs for acids are each of 1 litre capacity. The wide arm of the U-tube is graduated in 0·5 ml units for the range 0–10, and in 1·0 ml units for the range 10–250. Flask *F* is of 250 ml capacity.

Reagents

HCl, 250 ml/litre, approx. 3N

HCl, 166 ml/litre, approx. 2N, with trace of $KHgI_3$
$CaCO_3$

Procedure

Prepare the apparatus by decomposing about 1 g $CaCO_3$ with acid in the flask *F* when attached to the apparatus and leaving for half hour with taps *A* and *B* closed. This gives opportunity for CO_2 to dissolve in the manometer liquid and in acid in the reservoir. Replace flask with a similar one containing a weighed representative subsample of air-dry soil (< 2 mm or $< 0{\cdot}5$ mm as necessary). Suitable weights are:

20 g for soils (< 2 mm) containing 5% $CaCO_3$
10 g for soils (< 2 mm) containing 5–10% $CaCO_3$
5 g for soils ($< 0{\cdot}5$ mm) containing 10–20% $CaCO_3$
2 g for soils ($< 0{\cdot}5$ mm) containing 20–50% $CaCO_3$
1 g for soils ($< 0{\cdot}5$ mm) containing > 50% $CaCO_3$

Transfer the weighed subsample to flask *F*. Open tap *A* and insert moistened bung very firmly into flask *F*. Open tap *B* and raise water reservoir so that the level in both tubes rises just above zero graduation. Close tap *B* and lower reservoir to bench level. Close tap *A*. Open acid inlet tap *C*, running in enough acid to make the sample just fluid. Shake and allow to stand for several minutes. When reaction appears to have ceased open tap *B* and allow liquid in left-hand tube to become level with that in the graduated tube. Close tap *B*. Add further acid and shake well. Repeat this procedure until completion of the reaction and dissipation of heat are indicated by a constant equal level in the two adjacent tubes. A very slow reaction lasting more than 30 minutes can occur with dolomitic samples. Read the volume of gas evolved. Record air temperature and barometric pressure. Check recovery by using 1 g $CaCO_3$ instead of soil.

Calculation

The result is expressed as '$CaCO_3$ equivalent' because some samples contain $MgCO_3$.

% $CaCO_3$ equivalent in sample

$$= \frac{\text{volume of } CO_2 \text{ (ml)}}{\text{mass of sample (g)}} \times \frac{\text{barometric pressure (mm Hg)}}{\text{temperature (°C + 273)}} \times K$$

where

$$K = \frac{273 \times 100}{760 \times 224} = 0{\cdot}1604.$$

Report on oven-dry basis (Section 3.1.1).

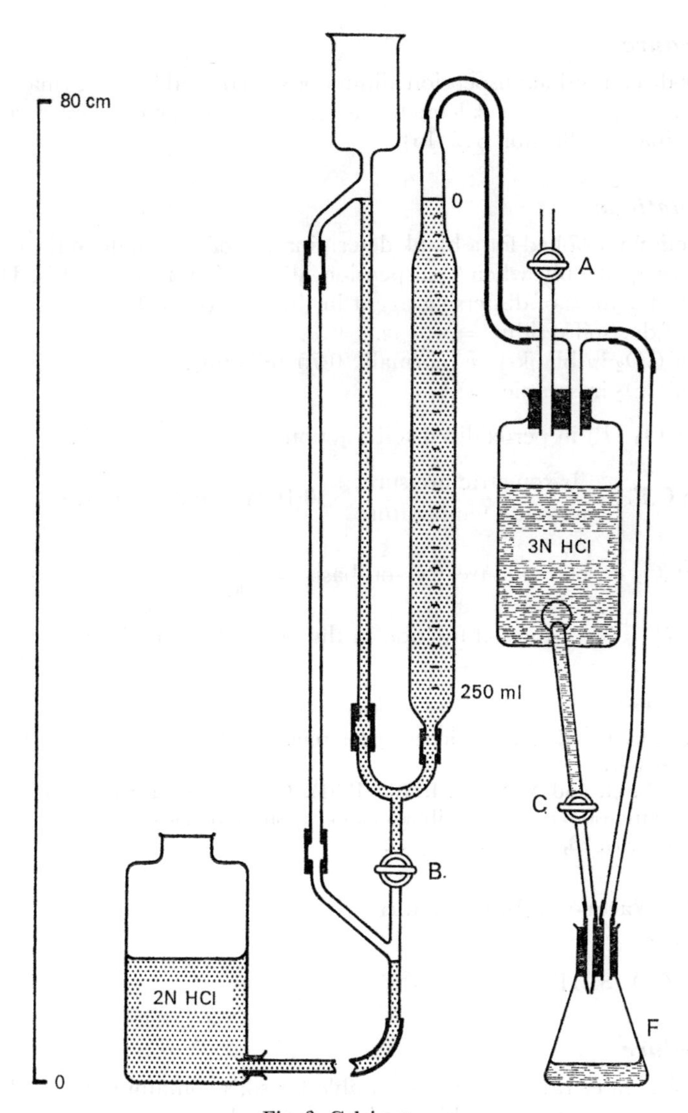

Fig. 3. Calcimeter.

(b) Carbonate and non-carbonate contents of particle-size fractions

Procedure

The dried residue, suspension aliquot or sieved sand fraction (mass xg), is treated with HCl in a calcimeter as described under calcium carbonate determination (Section 3.5.1a).

Calculations

Correction is applied for a blank determination of carbonate in the dispersing reagent only when a suspension aliquot is under analysis. Denote oven-dry mass of dispersing agent in the aliquot as m.

Mass of dry soil residue $= x - m$.

Vol. of CO_2 in blank $= v$ (normally 0·75–0·85 ml).

Vol. of CO_2 in sample $= V$.

$$\% \; CaCO_3 \; (Y) \text{ in peroxidized soil fraction} = \frac{(V - v)}{x - m} \times \text{C.F.}$$

$$\text{where C.F.} = \frac{\text{barometric pressure}}{\text{absolute temperature}} \times 0{\cdot}1604 \text{ (see Section 3.5.1).}$$

$$\% \; CaCO_3 \text{ on peroxide-treated soil basis} = \frac{YQ}{100}$$

where $Q = \%$ of the soil fraction in the peroxide-treated soil.

References

BASCOMB, C. L. (1961). A calcimeter for routine use on soil samples. *Chemy Ind.* 1826–7.

SHIELDS, L. G. and MEYER, M. W. (1964). Carbonate clay: measurement and relationship to clay distribution and cation-exchange capacity. *Proc. Soil Sci. Soc. Am.* **28,** 416–19.

3.5.2 Water-soluble gypsum

Reagent

$(CH_3)_2CO$ (S.L.R.)

Procedure

A soil: water ratio of 1 : 5 is suitable for soils containing up to 15 me/100 g, otherwise a greater dilution is necessary. For 1 : 5 extract shake 10 g air-dry soil in 50 ml water for 30 minutes.

Centrifuge, and pipette 20 ml aliquot of clear supernatant liquid into a 50 ml centrifuge tube. Add 20 ml $(CH_3)_2CO$, mix and allow to stand for 10 minutes while precipitate flocculates. Centrifuge, discard supernatant liquid and drain the tube. Dissolve precipitate in water and determine sulphate by method given in Section 3.5.3.

Reference

RICHARDS, L. A. (Ed.) (1954) Diagnosis and improvement of saline and alkali soils. U.S. Dept. Agric. Handb. 60.

3.5.3 Water-soluble sulphate

Reagents

HCl (conc.)
$BaCl_2.2H_2O$, 10% solution
Methyl orange, 0·01% solution

Procedure

Transfer the solution (or a suitable aliquot) from Section 3.5.2 to a 250 ml beaker and dilute to approx. 100 ml with water. Add 2 drops of methyl orange indicator and 0·5 ml HCl. Heat to boiling and add $BaCl_2$ solution dropwise with stirring until precipitation is complete. Cover and leave in warm place overnight. Filter through a tared Gooch crucible, dry at 105°C and then ignite at 650°C for 30 minutes. Cool in a desiccator and weigh.

Calculation

$$SO_4^{=} \text{ me/litre} = \frac{\text{mg } BaSO_4}{\text{ml aliquot}} \times 8{\cdot}568.$$

3.5.4 Acid-soluble sulphate

Reagents

As for Section 3.5.3.
NH_4OH (sp. gr. 0·88)

Procedure

Weigh 2·00 g air-dry soil into a 400 ml beaker and cover with a clock-glass. Add about 180 ml water and 20 ml HCl. If sample is calcareous care is necessary to control effervescence and an additional 0·5 ml HCl should be added for every 3% $CaCO_3$ present (Section 3.5.1). When all effervescence has ceased boil the suspension for 5 min. Rinse the clock-glass into the beaker. Filter through an 11 cm No. 41 paper into a 250 ml beaker. Add 2 drops of methyl orange indicator. Just neutralize by adding NH_4OH dropwise followed by 0·5 ml HCl. Continue procedure as in Section 3.5.3 starting at "Heat to boiling . . .".

Calculation

$SO_4^{=}$ % (air-dry basis) = $BaSO_4$ (g) × 20·58.
Report on oven-dry basis (Section 3.1.1).

Reference

BOWDEN, S. R. (1968). *Analysis of sulphate-bearing soils.* Current paper 3/68, Building Research Station, Garston, Hertfordshire.

3.6 EXTRACTABLE IRON, ALUMINIUM AND MANGANESE

3.6.1 Pyrophosphate extraction

Reagent

$K_4P_2O_7 . 3H_2O$, 0·1M

Procedure

100 ml $K_4P_2O_7$ solution is added to 1 g soil (< 2 mm air-dry) in a polythene bottle, stoppered and shaken overnight at room temperature. After centrifugation in the same vessel at 2000 rpm for 15 min (RCF* 415), the supernatant liquid is decanted into another bottle and retained. The residue is washed by shaking with approximately 20 ml distilled water, centrifuged and the supernatant discarded.

3.6.2 Pyrophosphate-extractable iron

(a) Colorimetric determination

Reagents

HNO_3, 8M
H_2SO_4, 9M

Procedure

A 1 ml aliquot of the extract is pipetted into a 25 ml conical flask, several drops of 8M HNO_3 and 10 drops of 9M H_2SO_4 added, and the mixture fumed down almost to dryness. If all organic coloration is not lost the procedure is repeated with more HNO_3. The contents are then transferred quantitatively to a 50 ml volumetric flask for Fe determination by the method given in Section 3.6.5.

(b) Atomic absorptiometric determination

* Relative centrifugal force.

Apparatus

Perkin Elmer 290 Spectrophotometer with 5 cm slot burner, using an oxidizing air/acetylene flame
Wavelengths: 248·3 nm (0–20 ppm) or 302·1 nm (0–50 ppm)

Reagent

Fe standard: Dissolve 0·100 g iron wire in a minimum of 6N HCl and dilute to 100 ml (≡ 1000 ppm Fe). Dilute aliquot × 10 for 100 ppm Fe standard.

Procedure

Prepare standard Fe solutions with concentration ranges 0–20 and 0–50 ppm by diluting aliquots of standard Fe solution to required volume with 0·1M $K_4P_2O_7 . 3H_2O$. Read standards and soil extracts on spectrophotometer. Plot graphs of scale reading against Fe content of standards.

Calculation

% extractable Fe in air-dry soil = ppm Fe from graph/100.
Report on oven-dry basis (Section 3.1.1).

Reference

PERKIN-ELMER CORP. *Analytical methods for atomic absorption spectrophotometry.* Norwalk, Conn., U.S.A.

3.6.3 Pyrophosphate-extractable aluminium

(a) Colorimetric determination

Apparatus

Thermostatically controlled water-bath

Reagents

Xylenol orange, 0·15% aqueous
Buffer solution pH 3·8: Dissolve 136 g NaOAc.$3H_2O$ in water, adjust to pH 3·8 with HCl and dilute to 1 litre.
E.D.T.A. (disodium salt), 0·05M
Cresol red, 0·1% in ethanol
NH_4OH solution, 5N approx.
Al standard: Dissolve 0·500 g Al by warming in 20 ml 1 : 1 HCl. Dilute to 1 litre. Dilute an aliquot × 100 to give standard 5 μg/ml.

Procedure

A 1 ml aliquot of the $K_4P_2O_7$ extract is fumed down with acids as for Fe determination (Section 3.6.2(a)). Hydrolyse the residue by adding 15 ml water and simmering on hot plate at boiling point for 1 hour (with bumping tube and cover glass). After cooling the contents are transferred quantitatively to a 100 ml volumetric flask to a volume not exceeding 50 ml. Add a few drops of cresol red and adjust to pH 2 approx. using 5N NH_4OH. Add 25 ml buffer solution and 10 ml xylenol orange. Place the flask in water bath at 40°C for 1½ hours, cool, add 5 ml E.D.T.A., make up to 100 ml and mix.

% Transmittance at 550 nm is recorded 1 hour later.

Prepare range of standards with 0 to 18 ml of standard Al solution in 100 ml flasks.

A blank determination on 1 ml $K_4P_2O_7$ is also made. Adjust pH, develop colour and read transmittance as above.

Prepare graph of μg Al/100 ml against % transmittance.

Calculation

$$\% \text{ Extractable Al in air-dry soil} = \frac{\mu\text{g Al read from graph}}{100}.$$

Report on oven-dry basis (Section 3.1.1).

(b) Atomic absorptiometric determination

Apparatus

Perkin Elmer 290 Spectrophotometer with 5 cm slot burner, using reducing nitrous oxide/acetylene flame

Reagent

Aluminium standard: Dissolve 1·00 g Al by warming in 20 ml 6N HCl, and dilute to 1 litre (≡ 100 ppm).

Procedure

Prepare standard Al solutions representing 0–50 ppm by diluting aliquots of standard Al solution to required volume with 0·1M $K_4P_2O_7$.

Read standards and soil extracts on spectrophotometer at 309·3 nm.

Plot graphs of scale reading against Al content of standards.

Calculation

% extractable Al in air-dry soil = ppm Al from graph/100.

Report on oven-dry basis (Section 3.1.1).

References

PERKIN-ELMER CORP. *Analytical methods for atomic absorption spectrophotometry.* Norwalk, Conn., U.S.A.

PRITCHARD, D. T. (1967). Spectrophotometric determination of aluminium in soil extracts with xylenol orange. *Analyst, Lond.* **92,** 103–6.

3.6.4 Dithionite extraction

Reagents

Buffer pH 3·8: Mix 1 litre M CH_3COONa with 390 ml CH_3COOH (glacial) and dilute to 2·5 litre with water.

$Na_2S_2O_4$, powder (S.L.R.)

Procedure

(a) < 2 mm air-dry soil

Weigh 1 g < 2 mm soil into a 250 ml polythene screwcap bottle. Add 100 ml buffer by pipette and 4 g (approx.) sodium dithionite, cap and immediately place on shaker overnight (16 hours). Start of shaking should not be delayed as $Na_2S_2O_4$ decomposes rather rapidly in solution. Centrifuge and carefully decant all of the supernatant liquid into a stoppered flask.

(b) Residue after pyrophosphate extraction

Use washed residue from Section 3.6.1 and proceed as above starting from "Add 100 ml buffer . . .".

3.6.5 Dithionite-extractable iron

(a) Colorimetric determination

Reagents

NH_4OH, 4N

$HSCH_2CO_2H$ (thioglycollic acid), 10% solution just neutralized by addition of NH_4OH solution

Fe standard: Dissolve 0·100 g iron wire in HCl and dilute to 1 litre (0·1 mg Fe/ml). Dilute aliquot × 10 for 0·01 mg/ml standard.

Procedure

Pipette a 1 ml aliquot of the extract into a 50 ml volumetric flask, add about 20 ml water and mix. Then add 1 ml 10% thioglycollic acid solution and 5 ml NH_4OH solution. Swirl the contents of the flask, unstoppered, until oxidation and full colour development have taken place, then make up to the mark with water and mix. Measure transmittance at 530 nm. Prepare standard range by pipetting 1 to 10 ml of 0·01 mg/ml standard into series of 50 ml volumetric flasks, add reagents, develop colour and read as above. Prepare standard graph of mg Fe/50 ml against absorbance.

Calculation

% Extractable Fe in air-dry soil = 10 × mg Fe read off graph.
Report on oven-dry basis (Section 3.1.1).

(b) Atomic absorptiometric determination

Apparatus and reagents as for Section 3.6.2b.

Procedure

Prepare blank solution by placing 4 g sodium dithionite in a 100 ml volumetric flask, dissolve in buffer pH 3·8 (Section 3.6.4) and make up to volume with the same solution.

Prepare standard Fe solutions representing ranges 0–20 and 0–50 ppm Fe by pipetting aliquots of standard Fe solution into 100 ml volumetric flasks, add 10 ml blank solution (freshly made) to each flask. Make up to volume with water. Pipette 5 ml aliquot of soil extract into a 50 ml volumetric flask and make up with water.

Read standards and soil extracts on spectrophotometer at 302·1 nm (50 ppm range), or 248·3 nm (20 ppm range).

Plot graph of scale reading against Fe content of standards.

Calculation

% Extractable Fe in air-dry soil = ppm Fe from graph × dilution/100.
Report on oven-dry basis (Section 3.1.1).

References

Kilmer, V. J. (1960). The estimation of free iron oxides in soils. *Proc. Soil Sci. Soc Am.* **24,** 420–1.

Perkin-Elmer Corp. *Analytical methods for atomic absorption spectrophotometry.* Norwalk, Conn., U.S.A.

Yuan, T. L. and Breland, H. L. (1969). Evaluation of atomic absorption methods for determinations of aluminium, iron, and silicon in clay and soil extracts. *Proc. Soil Sci. Soc. Am.* **33,** 868–72.

3.6.6 Dithionite-extractable manganese

Reagents

H_2O_2, 27–30%
H_3PO_4 (density 1·75)
KIO_4
H_2SO_4, 9N
Standard Mn solution: Dissolve 0·2878 g of $KMnO_4$ in about 250 ml water in a 1 litre volumetric flask. Add 80 ml 9N H_2SO_4 and decolorize the $KMnO_4$ by adding freshly prepared 2% $Na_2S_2O_4$ solution. Oxidize the excess H_2SO_3 by adding concentrated HNO_3. Cool and dilute to volume. The solution contains 0·1 mg Mn/ml.

Procedure

Pipette a 20 ml aliquot of centrifuged $Na_2S_2O_4$ extract of soil into a 125 ml conical beaker. Add 5 ml H_2O_2 followed by 10 ml 9N H_2SO_4. Evaporate to fumes of H_2SO_4. Add 5 ml H_2O_2 (or more as necessary to decolorize) and evaporate to fumes. Cool, rinse with distilled water and evaporate to fumes. Add 5 ml H_3PO_4 and 35 ml of distilled water. Heat to boiling, add 0·3 g KIO_4. Cover and maintain a temperature of 90–100°C for half an hour. Cool, transfer to 50 ml volumetric flask, dilute to volume and mix. Measure absorbance at 525 nm. Prepare a calibration graph covering the range 0–10 μg Mn/ml.

Calculation

$$\% \text{ Extractable Mn in air-dry soil} = \frac{\mu\text{g Mn read off graph}}{40}.$$

Report on oven-dry basis (Section 3.1.1).

Reference

Pruden, G. and King, H. G. C. (1969). A scheme of semi-micro analysis for the major elements in clay minerals, based on modifications to conventional methods of silicate analysis. *Clay Minerals*, **8,** 1–13.

3.7 SALINITY

3.7.1 Preparation of saturation extract

Apparatus

Straight-sided sample glass of diameter only slightly greater than conductivity cell (Section 3.7.2)

Procedure

Place approx. 20 g < 2 mm air-dry soil in a 50 ml beaker and add just sufficient water to saturate, stir gently, cover and leave to stand overnight. Stir again and use small amounts of dry soil or water to achieve the following criteria:

1. Tap beaker on bench; free water should not separate on the surface of the soil.
2. Soil paste glistens as it reflects light.
3. Soil paste flows slightly when container is tipped.
4. Soil paste slides freely and cleanly off a spatula, except in the case of heaviest clays.

To minimize puddling of fine textured soils, too much stirring should be avoided. Transfer the saturated paste on to a toughened filter paper in a Buchner funnel, apply suction and collect filtrate in the sample glass.

Reference

Richards, L. A. (Ed.) (1954). Diagnosis and improvement of saline and alkali soils. U.S. Dept. Agr. Handb. 60.

3.7.2 Conductivity of saturation extract

Apparatus

Conductivity bridge and cell

Procedure

Insert the conductivity cell into the filtered extract contained in the sample glass. Record the conductivity meter reading (R_t ohms), the temperature of the extract and the cell constant.

Calculation

Conductivity meter readings need to be corrected to 25°C using the temperature factor f_t given in Table 5.

$$\text{Conductivity m mho/cm (25°C)} = \frac{\text{Cell constant} \times 100}{R_t \text{ (ohms)}} \times f_t.$$

3.7.3 Sodium in saturation extract

Procedure

Pipette an appropriate aliquot of the saturation extract into a volumetric flask, make up to mark with distilled water and mix. Proceed as in Section 3.3.5 except that standard Na solutions are made up in water, not NH_4OAc, for calibration.

Calculation

ppm Na in saturation extract =

$$\text{ppm measured in diluted extract} \times \frac{\text{volume of flask (ml)}}{\text{volume of aliquot (ml)}}.$$

TABLE 5

Temperature Factors for Correction of Conductivity Meter Readings

°C	f_t	°C	f_t	°C	f_t
12·0	1·341	19·0	1·136	23·0	1·043
13·0	1·309	19·5	1·125	23·5	1·032
14·0	1·277	20·0	1·112	24·0	1·020
15·0	1·247	20·5	1·100	24·5	1·010
16·0	1·218	21·0	1·087	25·0	1·000
17·0	1·189	21·5	1·075	25·5	0·995
18·0	1·163	22·0	1·064	26·0	0·979
18·5	1·150	22·5	1·053	26·5	0·974

4 Density and Water-release Characteristics

P. D. Smith and A. J. Thomasson

Undisturbed samples for bulk density and water release measurements are normally taken from non-stony and moderately stony soil horizons using a special coring device (Dagg and Hosegood 1962) constructed to fit sampling tins 76 mm in diameter and 51 mm high (Plate IIb). Three replicate cores are collected from each horizon sampled. Measurements on soils too stony for coring are described in Sections 4.1.2 and 4.2.4.

To determine the bulk density of peat and other soft, easily compressible soils, samples can be taken in rectangular boxes (Kubiena boxes), as described in Section 2.3.

Reference

Dagg, M. and Hosegood, P. H. (1962). Details of a hand sampling tool for taking undisturbed soil cores. *E. afr. agric. For. J.* Supplement to Special issue, 129–31.

4.1 DENSITY

4.1.1 Bulk density (non-stony soil)

The bulk density of soil (D_b) is calculated from the mass of oven-dry soil (M_d) and its field volume (V).

$$D_b = \frac{M_d}{V} \text{ (g cm}^{-3}\text{)}.$$

This measurement is essential to express water release determinations in terms of volume. The oven-dry mass of three replicate cores is summed and divided by the total volume (666 cm^3).

As a separate determination it may be more convenient to use a larger single core of the order of 700 to 1000 cm^3. The coring cylinder should have a sharpened forward edge, and a diameter approximately 1·5 times its length. The cylinder is hammered vertically into the soil until full and the contents weighed after drying at 105°C.

Large samples for bulk density can also be obtained from a Proline monolith (Plate I) using a semi-circular template and hack-saw. By this method a complete profile of bulk density measurements can be obtained. Small errors in measuring the volume are counterbalanced by the increased accuracy of a bulk density value derived from a larger sample. Bulk density is normally expressed to the second decimal place (*e.g.* 1·32 g cm^{-3}), so the accuracy of mass or volume measurements need not exceed 1%.

4.1.2 **Bulk density of fine earth** (stony soil)—D_{bf}

In soils which can be cored, stones may be screened after oven drying. The size of the core must be considered in relation to the diameter of the stones (Table 1, p. 3). The volume of stones (V_s) is calculated from their mass and bulk density, as described in Section 4.1.4.

$$D_{bf}\ (\text{g cm}^{-3}) = \frac{M_d - M_s}{V - V_s}$$

where M_d is the total mass of oven-dry soil,
V its total field volume,
M_s is the mass of stones,
and V_s is the volume of stones.

Core sampling becomes impracticable when stones exceed about 10% by volume or their diameters exceed 2 cm. For soils with up to 30% stones less than 6 cm in diameter, a sample volume of 20 litres can be obtained by the replacement method, as follows.

Apparatus

3000 plastic balls 2 cm in diameter (Appendix, p. 82)
Spade
Spring balance (50 ± 0·2 kg)
Plastic bucket (8 litres)
Polythene sheet
Marine plywood board with a square hole 30 × 30 cm
Graduated cylinder (5 litres)
Sieve (6 or 20 mm square mesh)

Procedure

Place the board on the soil or horizon surface and dig out a hole about 20 cm deep using the board as a template and avoiding compaction of the sides. Place all excavated soil and stones on the polythene sheet. The field mass of soil and stones (M) must be determined immediately. Subsamples of fine earth for determination of gravimetric water content (θ_f) and bulk density of stones (D_{bs}) (Section 4.1.4) are taken and sealed in polythene bags. If field water content and texture allow, stones can be sieved and weighed in the field (M_s). Soils which cannot be sieved in the field must be transported to the laboratory and wet sieved to determine the mass of stones.

The volume of soil removed is measured by pouring the plastic balls into the hole until level with the soil surface. The number of balls remaining may be counted individually or estimated by using the measuring cylinder. The number of balls required to fill a known volume should be calibrated separately for a range of large and small volumes. Those used by the Survey have a packing density of 1 ball per 7·315 cm for volumes of 10 to 20 litres when allowed to settle randomly.

Calculations

(1) Volume of hole

$$V = \frac{\text{No. of balls} \times 7{\cdot}315}{1000} \qquad \text{(litres).}$$

(2) Field moisture content of fine earth

$$\theta_f = \frac{M_f - M_{df}}{M_{df}} \qquad \text{(\% mass)}$$

where M_f = mass of subsample of fine earth at field moisture content
and M_{df} = mass of subsample of oven-dry fine earth.
(3) Oven-dry mass of excavated fine earth

$$M_{df} = \frac{100(M - M_s)}{100 + \theta_f} \qquad \text{(kg).}$$

(4) Volume of stones excavated

$$V_s = \frac{M_s}{D_{bs}} \qquad \text{(litres).}$$

Hence, the bulk density of the fine earth

$$D_{bf} = \frac{M_{df}}{V - V_s} \qquad (\text{g cm}^{-3} \text{ or kg litre}^{-1})$$

and the % volume of stones $= \dfrac{100V_s}{V}$.

If a 6 or 20 mm sieve is used, D_{bf} is not the bulk density of fine earth as usually defined (< 2 mm). It is commonly impracticable to screen a large volume of soil through a 2 mm sieve without breaking down a proportion of the stones. A small proportion of stones in the 2 to 6 or 10 mm range will not greatly affect the bulk density value. If it is essential to determine the D_b of the < 2 mm fine earth in a soil where large stones preclude a small sample volume, an appropriately sized subsample (Table 1, p. 3) of material passing the larger sieve may be screened, and the proportion of stones added to the values for M_s and V_s.

4.1.3 Particle density

Apparatus

Specific gravity bottles (25 ml—BS733 MBL)
Pestle and mortar or grinding mill
Vacuum pump desiccator
Constant temperature water bath (20°C ± 0·5°C)
Drying oven (105°C ± 1°C)
Balance (± 0·001 g)

Procedure

Weigh a clean dry specific gravity bottle with its stopper in position (M_1). Fill the bottle with de-aerated water and immerse in the water bath. Top up the bottle as necessary with water maintained at the same temperature. When no further topping up is required, carefully dry the exterior of the bottle and weigh (M_2). Empty the bottle and dry using acetone. Grind a representative sample of fine earth to break down all aggregates larger than 0·2 mm, oven-dry, place about 2 g of the ground soil in the bottle and weigh (M_3). Add about 10 ml of water to the soil, agitate the bottle, and place it without its stopper in a desiccator under vacuum. At intervals of about 2 hours, remove the bottle and replace in the desiccator. After about 6 hours, fill the bottle to the bottom of its neck with water, agitate it, and replace in the desiccator. After 24 hours, place the bottle in the water bath. The following day, top up the bottle with water at 20°C, insert stopper, dry the exterior and weigh (M_4).

Coarse particles of organic matter tend to float on the surface of the water and interfere with insertion of the stopper. This can be overcome by adding one or two drops of liquid detergent to the water. The density of the water is not changed significantly but its surface tension will be lessened, causing the organic matter to sink.

Calculations

Volume of bottle

$$V_b = \frac{M_2 - M_1}{D_w} \qquad \text{(ml)}$$

where D_w is the density of water.
Mass of soil

$$M_{df} = M_3 - M_1 \qquad \text{(g)}.$$

Volume of soil particles

$$V_p = V_b - \frac{M_4 - M_3}{D_w} \qquad \text{(ml)}.$$

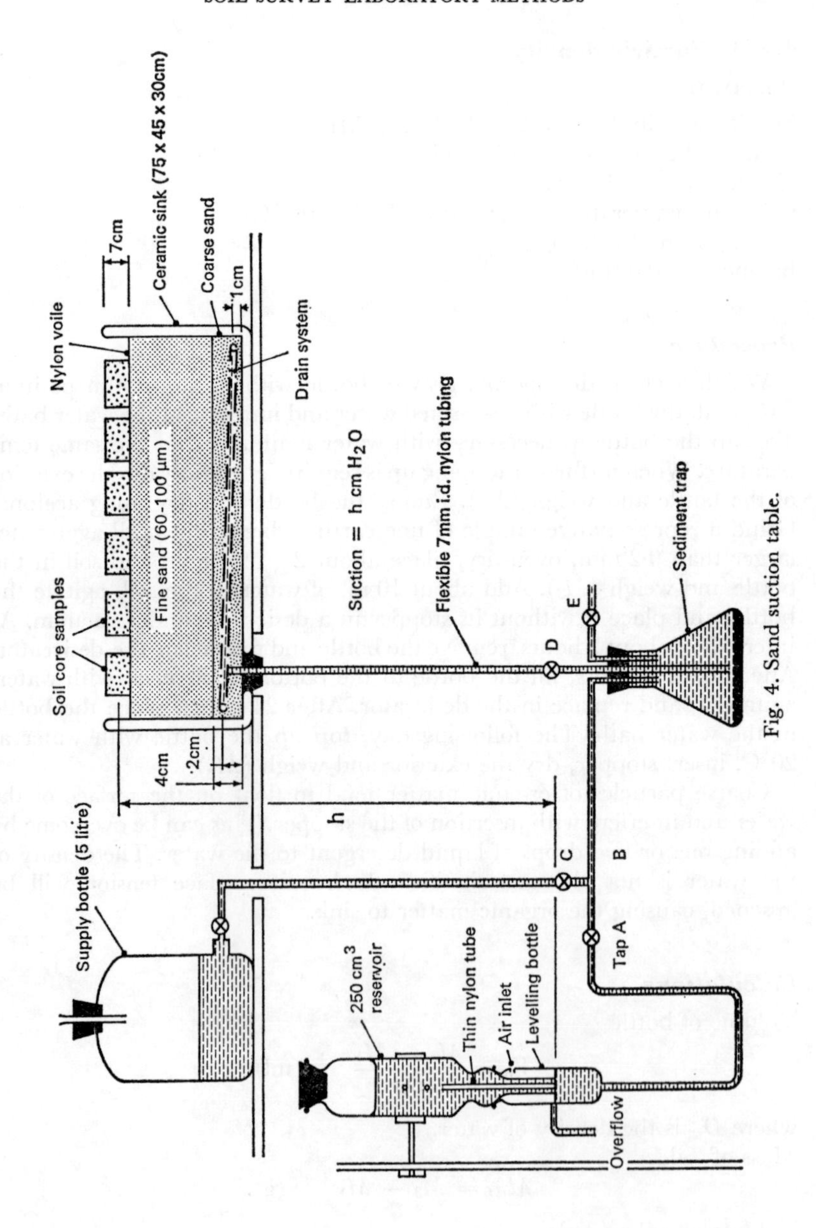

Fig. 4. Sand suction table.

Particle density

$$D_p = \frac{M_{df}}{V_p} \qquad (\text{g cm}^{-3}).$$

4.1.4 Density and porosity of stones

Many stones found in soils are virtually non-porous (*e.g.* flint and most quartzite pebbles) and their bulk density is equivalent to their particle density. Most limestones, chalk and many sandstones have a smaller bulk density and appreciable porosity. Provided the stones contain little iron and are non-porous, a density of 2·7 can be assumed, but density and porosity should be measured if there is any uncertainty.

Apparatus

Desiccator
Vacuum pump
Drying oven
Balance (top-loading ± 0·01 g)

Procedure

Wash a representative stone to remove loose soil and mark with waterproof ink. Half submerge the stone in de-aerated water in a desiccator under vacuum. After 24 hours submerge the stone completely and leave under vacuum for a further 24 hours.

Weigh a beaker of water (M_1). Tie a length of nylon thread round the stone, dip it in acetone, and shake to remove excess water and acetone. Weigh the stone quickly (M_2) and then weigh the beaker of water with the stone suspended in it (M_3). Oven dry the stone and reweigh (M_4).

Particle density of the stone (D_p) may be determined by grinding through a 2 mm sieve and proceeding as for soil samples (Section 4.1.3).

Calculations

Volume of stone

$$V_s = \frac{M_3 - M_1}{D_w} \qquad (\text{cm}^3)$$

where D_w is the density of water.
Bulk density of stone

$$D_{bs} = \frac{M_4}{V_s} \qquad (\text{g cm}^{-3}).$$

Porosity

$$P = \left(\frac{M_2 - M_4}{D_w V_s}\right) 100 \qquad (\%\ \text{vol}).$$

Porosity may also be calculated from the particle density of the stones

$$P = \left(1 - \frac{D_b}{D_p}\right) 100 \qquad (\% \text{ vol}).$$

4.2 WATER-RELEASE CHARACTERISTICS

(core samples)

The soil must be brought to a suction smaller than 50 mb before starting work. A range of apparatus is required enabling large samples (222 cm^3) to be treated at smaller suctions where soil heterogeneity is greatest, and smaller samples to be used at larger suctions (pressures) where equilibration time becomes critical.

4.2.1 Construction of sand and kaolin suction tables (after van der Haarst and Stakman 1965)

Materials

Large ceramic sink (*c.* 50 × 70 × 25 cm)
Nylon tubing 7 mm i.d.
Transparent PVC tubing 7 mm i.d.
'L' and 'T' pieces to fit tubing
Large rubber bung to fit sink outlet
Coarse sand, 600–2000 μm
Fine sand, 60–100 μm (Ground silica flour, Appendix, p. 82)
Coarse silt, 20–60 μm (Ground silica flour, Appendix, p. 82)
Kaolin (Appendix, p. 82)
Nylon voile
Glassware: stopcocks, levelling bottle, sediment trap, supply bottle

Procedure (Sand suction table, Fig. 4)

Construct a drain system from nylon tubing as shown in Fig. 5 to fit the floor of the sink, allowing 2 cm margin from the walls. Cement all joints with 'Araldite'. Cut slits 1 cm long in the underside of the tubing at 1 to 2 cm spacing. Wrap the tubes in 3 layers of nylon voile. Fit PVC tubing through the bung to the drain system and cement the bung into the sink outlet. Ensure that the drain system slopes upwards to a point above the outlet. Assemble glassware and external tubing as in Fig. 4. Fill all tubes and the sediment trap with water, and half fill the sink. Close taps *A*, *C* and *E*; open tap *D*.

Disconnect the tubing at point *B* and connect to a 5 l aspirator bottle and vacuum pump. Pour sufficient clean coarse sand into the sink to cover the drain system to about 1 cm, ensuring that the slope towards the outlet is retained within the sand. Add about 3 cm of saturated fine sand. Turn on the vacuum to draw off water, but maintain the water level well above the sand surface. When no air bubbles are visible in the tube below the sink outlet, add a second layer of saturated fine sand. Repeatedly add fine sand and draw off included air until the sand surface is about 7 cm from the top of the sink, ensuring that at all times the surface is submerged under water. It is best to recycle water from the vacuum aspirator as this contains less air than fresh tap water. De-airing should continue at intervals for a few days after filling is completed, until there is no evidence of air in the system. Finally, close tap *D*, empty the sediment trap, refill with water, open *D*, bleed off air using tap *E*, reconnect the tubes to supply and levelling bottles, set the suction at 100 mb, open tap *A*, and drain off surplus water. Place a sheet of nylon voile on the sand surface while it is still wet.

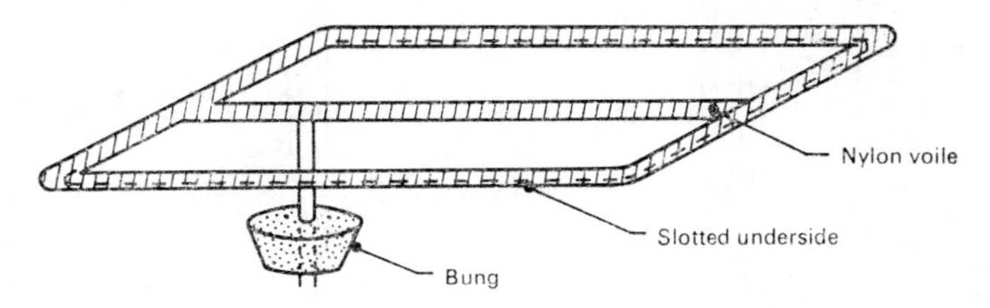

Fig. 5. Drain system for sand and kaolin suction table.

To test that the sand has an air entry value in excess of 100 mb suction, leave the levelling bottle at 100 mb for 2 days; raise the level at 10 min intervals by 20 cm until the surface is flooded, reconnect the vacuum source and check that no air appears at the outlet tube. After the test, change over to distilled or de-ionized water throughout the system.

The exact particle-size distribution of the fine sand is not critical provided that the 60–100 μm fraction is dominant. Using ground silica flour (Appendix, p. 82) mainly in this size range, remove all material finer than 20 μm by sedimentation as this reduces the permeability of the suction table. Any material coarser than 200 μm should be removed by sieving. During the later stages of filling the sink, fine material may accumulate on the surface or in suspension. This can be allowed to settle overnight and scraped off before recommencing filling.

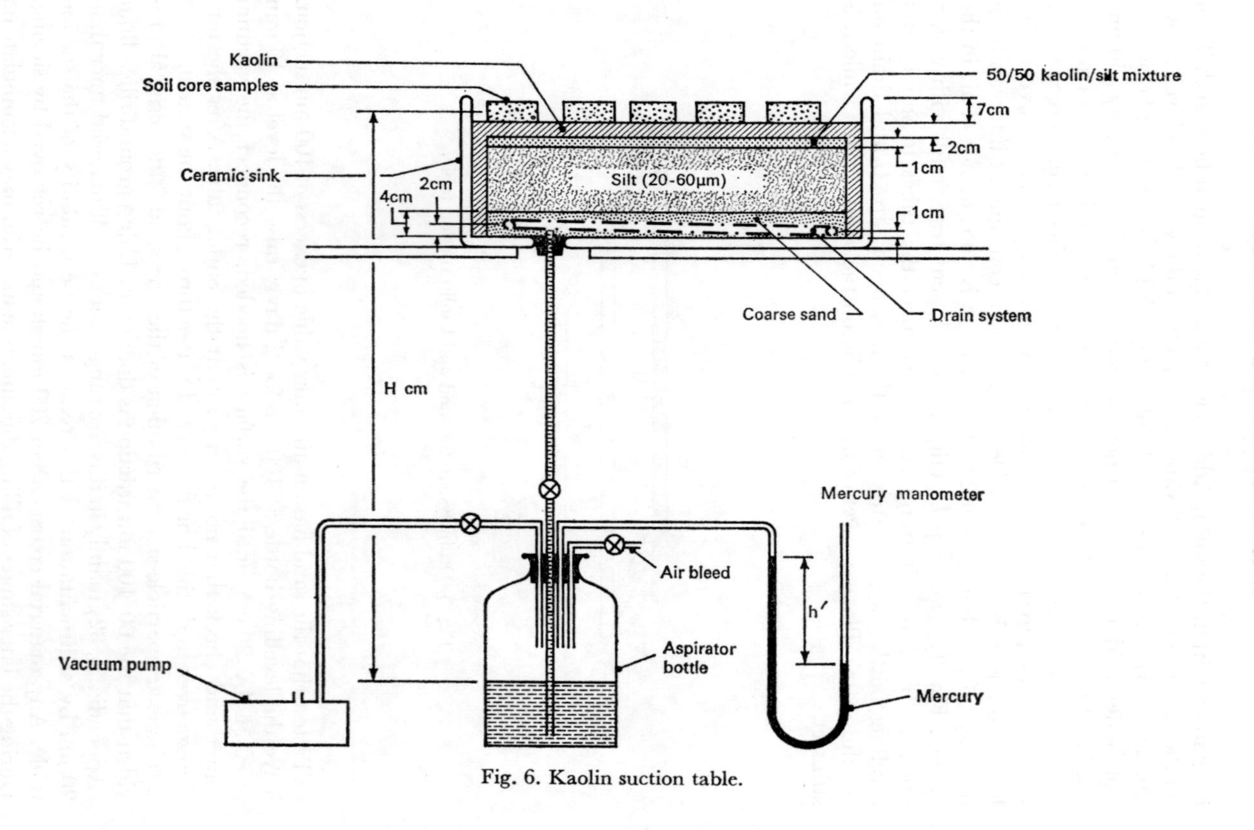

Fig. 6. Kaolin suction table.

Procedure (Kaolin suction table, Fig. 6)

The kaolin suction table is constructed in much the same way as the sand suction table. Kaolin, thoroughly mixed with water, is used to line the walls of the sink before adding the coarse sand. Coarse silt (20–60 μm) is then added up to about 10 cm from the surface. At this stage the de-airing procedure should be rigorously applied until no air is present in the silt. A mixture of wet kaolin and silt is spread over the whole surface about 1 cm thick, followed by a 2 cm layer of pure kaolin puddled to a stiff consistency. The water level should be lowered while the clay is pressed firmly on to the surface and smoothed off with a trowel. The surface is flooded from above, and de-airing continued for a few days at hourly intervals. Once the system is air-free, drain off the surface by setting the suction to 400 mb, using the vacuum pump, aspirator bottle and mercury manometer according to the formula:

$$\text{Suction} = 13{\cdot}6h' + H \qquad \text{cm } H_2O$$
$$= 0{\cdot}978(13{\cdot}6h' + H) \qquad \text{mb.}$$

Dimensions are indicated in Fig. 6.

Reference

HAARST, G. G. VAN DER and STAKMAN, W. P. (1965). *Soil moisture retention curves. II. Directions for the use of the sand-box apparatus, range pF* 0 *to* 2·7. Inst. Land and Water Management Research, Wageningen.

4.2.2 **Water retained at 50 to 400 mb suctions** (using suction tables)

The sand table is used to equilibrate at 50 to 100 mb suction and the kaolin table at 400 mb suction. Cores of 222 cm^3 are used throughout this range.

Procedure

Soil cores (4 above) are prepared by removing one lid and securing a piece of nylon voile over the exposed end with an elastic band. The core is weighed to ± 0·05 g, placed on a sand suction table set at 50 mb suction, and reweighed after 24 hours. Cores which lose weight are maintained at 50 mb suction and weighed daily until equilibrated. Cores which gain weight are taken off the suction table and placed on a saturated foam rubber surface for a few days and then returned to the suction table. A core is equilibrated at 50 mb suction when its daily weight loss is less than 0·05 g. It is then moved to a higher suction. Cores normally require at least 7 days to equilibrate at each suction, and in some cases up to 20 days.

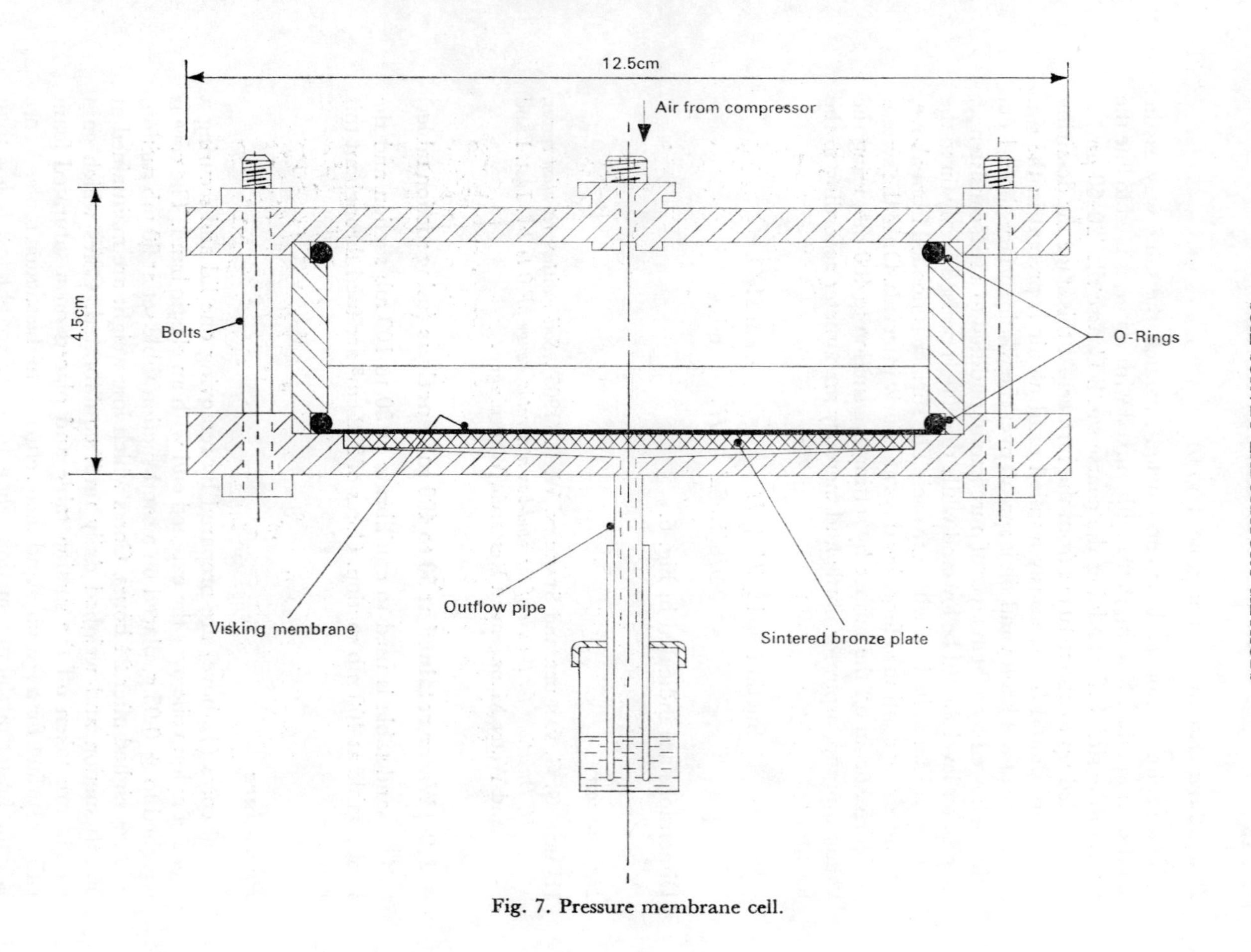

Fig. 7. Pressure membrane cell.

Plate III

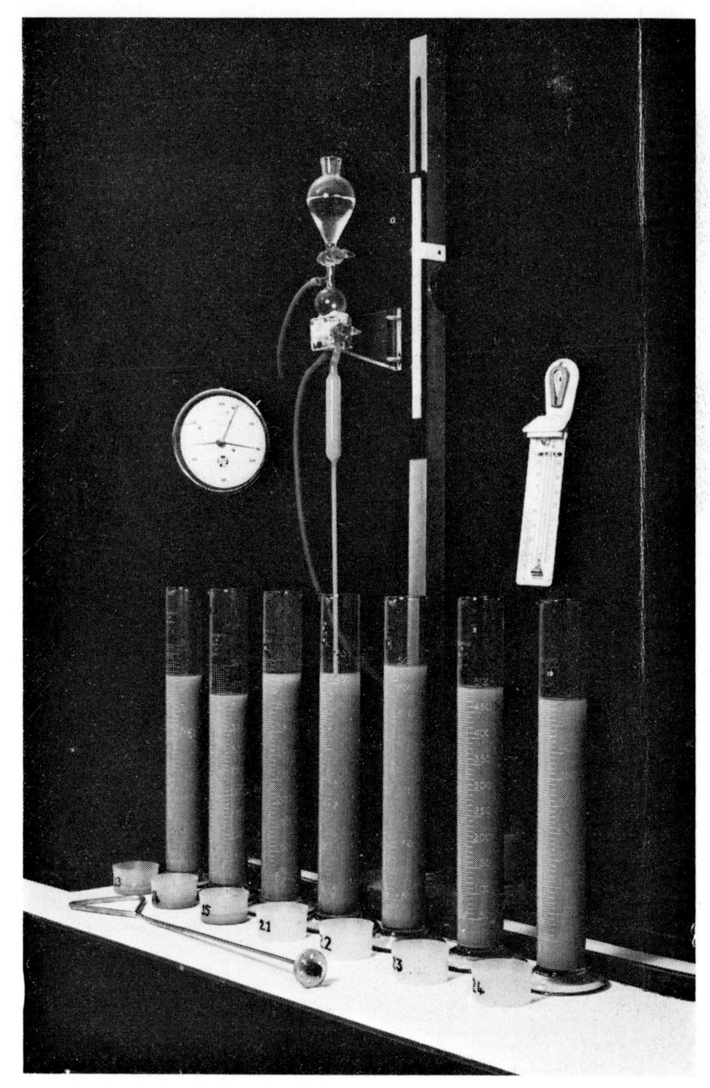

Sedimentation apparatus for particle-size analysis.

Plate IV

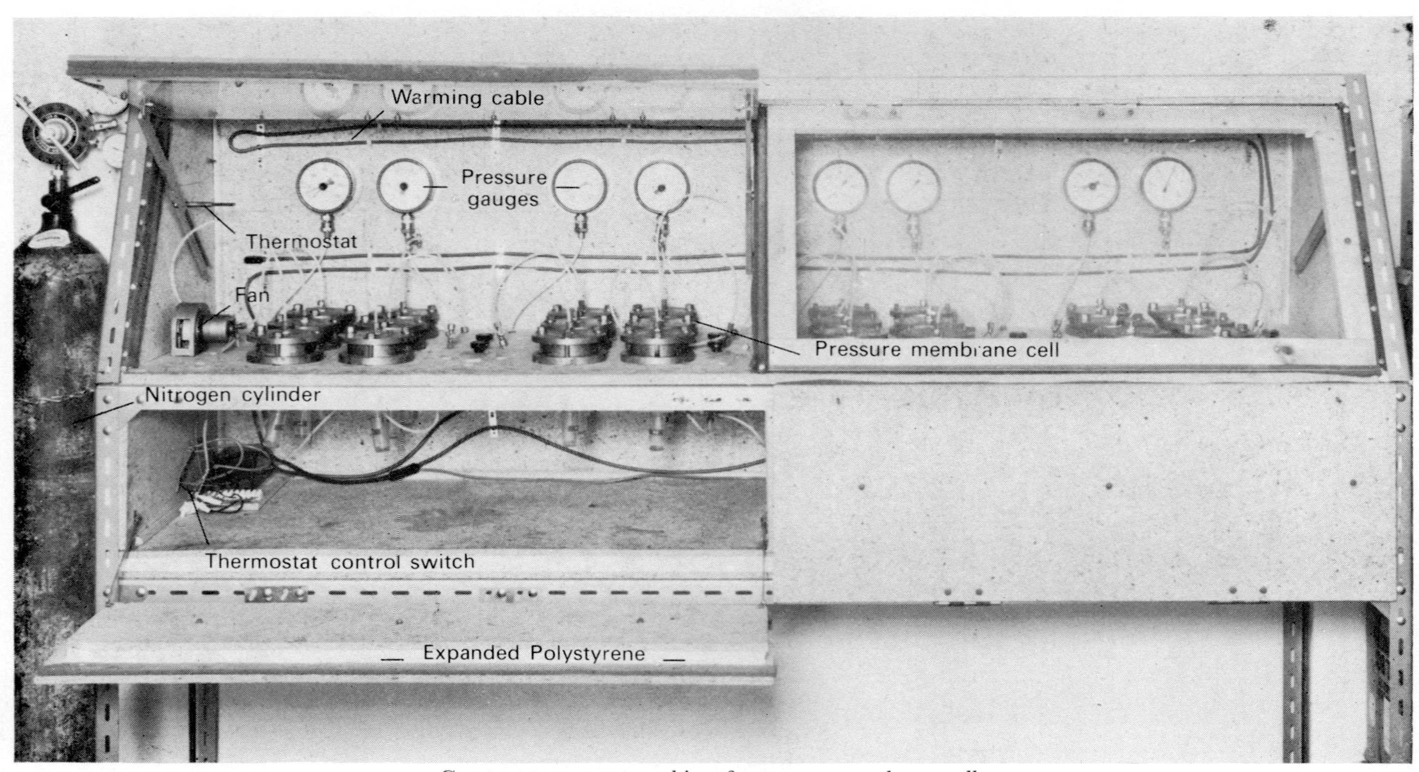

Constant temperature cabinet for pressure membrane cells.

Calculations

Measurements of water content are first expressed in terms of mass (%) of oven-dry soil and converted to volume using the bulk density value (Section 4.1.1) for the core as a whole. Values for horizons are calculated from the mean of three replicates.

Basic quantities

$S(s)$ = Equilibrated mass of soil and retained water at each suction (mb) *e.g.* S (50), S (100), S (400).

Sd = Mass of oven-dry soil.

$\theta_m(s)$ = Water content, % mass, at each suction

$$= \left(\frac{S(s) - Sd}{Sd}\right) 100.$$

$\theta_v(s)$ = Water content, % volume, at each suction

= $\theta_m(s) \times D_b$ (assuming the density of water is 1 g cm^{-3}).

4.2.3 **Water retained at 2 and 15 bar suctions** (using pressure membrane cells)

At these suctions it is impracticable to use samples larger than 50 cm^3 for routine work, and unsieved, little disturbed, soil is preferable. All moisture release measurements should be made in a room with minimum temperature fluctuation (± 2°C). Failing this, the pressure membrane cells should be housed in a constant temperature cabinet (Plate IV).

Apparatus

Pressure cells (Fig. 7) with porous bronze base plates
Air compressor (250 p.s.i.) or nitrogen cylinder
Drying oven (105 ± 0·5°C)
Balance (± 0·001 g)
Visking cellulose membrane
Specimen bottles, with tubes fitted to outlet of pressure cells—'outflow bottles'

Procedure

Cut a circular disc of Visking membrane to fit the pressure cell; soak in water for 5 min and place in cell. Using a moist knife, cut a slice of soil about 1 cm thick across the core sample and place centrally on the membrane. For non-cohesive sandy soils, a disturbed sample can be transferred to the cell using a spatula.

Separate samples for equilibration at 2 and 15 bar are taken from each core. Assemble the pressure cell; raise the pressure as required and check for leaks using detergent foam. Weigh the outflow bottle daily to $\pm$ 0·001 g. When a decrease of greater than 0·005 g (due to evaporation loss from the bottle) occurs on two successive days, the sample is considered to be equilibrated. It is then removed from the cell, weighed, $P_w(p)$, oven dried, and reweighed, $P_d(p)$.

Calculations

All measurements are first expressed in terms of mass of oven-dry soil, and converted to a volume basis using bulk density values (Section 4.1.1) for the whole (222 cm³) core.

Basic quantities

$P_w(p)$ = Equilibrated mass of soil and retained water at pressure p

$P_d(p)$ = Oven-dry mass of soil equilibrated at pressure p

$\theta_m(p)$ = Water content, % mass at pressure p

hence

$$\theta_m(2) = \frac{P_w(2) - P_d(2)}{P_d(2)} \times 100 \qquad \text{at 2 bars.}$$

and

$$\theta_m(15) = \frac{P_w(15) - P_d(15)}{P_d(15)} \times 100 \qquad \text{at 15 bars.}$$

If D_b = bulk density of original 222 cm³ core then

$$\theta_v(p) = \theta_m(p) \times D_b.$$

Derived quantities

T = Total pore space

$$= \left(1 - \frac{D_b}{D_p}\right) 100 \qquad (\% \text{ volume})$$

where D_p is particle density (Section 4.1.3).

$C_a(s)$ = Air capacity, % volume of pores empty of water at suction s.
$= T - \theta_v(s)$.

C_a is most commonly quoted for 50 mb suction. It represents the volume of pores greater than approximately 60 μm, sometimes referred to as macropores. Under British conditions, water retained at 50 mb suction approximates to field capacity (water retained 48 hours after saturation) except in permeable soils with shallow groundwater, peaty soils, and clay soils containing much expanding lattice clay. It is a useful equipotential value to compare one soil with another, and the difference between θ (50 mb) and θ (15 bar) represents, for most soils, the water available to plants.

The term A is used for this quantity.

$$A_m = \theta_m \text{ (50 mb)} - \theta_m \text{ (15 bar)} \qquad \text{(\% oven-dry mass).}$$
$$A_v = \theta_v \text{ (50 mb)} - \theta_v \text{ (15 bar)} \qquad \text{(\% volume)}$$
$$= A_m \times D_b \qquad \text{(\% volume).}$$

References

RICHARDS, L. A. (1947). Pressure-membrane apparatus—construction and use. *Agric. Engng, St. Joseph, Mich.* **28,** 451–4.
RICHARDS, L. A. (Ed.) (1954). Diagnosis and improvement of saline and alkali soils. U.S. Dept. Agric. Handb. 60.

4.2.4 Procedure for stony soils

Stones (> 6 mm) should not form part of the pressure membrane sample. After oven drying the volume of stones in the original core should be determined and a correction made to θ_v values to convert to % volume of total soil (θ_{vt}).

$$\theta_{vt} = \frac{\theta\,(100 - V_s)}{100}$$

where θ is the water content of the pressure membrane sample at equilibrium.

Thus in a soil containing 5% of non-porous stones by volume

$$\theta_{vt} = \frac{\theta_v \times 95}{100}$$

The reverse correction, to convert all values to a fine earth basis, is usually required for θ_v values at 50, 100 and 400 mb for soil including stones greater than 6 mm. This takes the form

$$\theta_{vf} = \frac{\theta_v \times 100}{(100 - V_s)}$$

where θ is water content of the core sample at equilibrium.

Thus in a soil containing 5% of non-porous stones by volume

$$\theta_{vf} = \frac{\theta_{vt} \times 100}{95}.$$

Porous stones require a further correction and a measurement of θ_v for the stones. In soils containing many very porous stones (pores > 30%), it is best to consider the stones as part of the soil mass, and not seek to distinguish θ_{vf} from θ_{vt}.

For mixtures of porous and non-porous stones, as in clay soils containing both flint and chalk fragments, increased replication and a quotation of results for the whole soil is recommended.

Hitherto relatively small corrections to determinations for soils which can be sampled in 222 cm^3 cores have been considered. Where this is impossible, a field capacity measurement (48 hours after saturation) may be combined with measurement of stone content and bulk density of the fine earth as in Section 4.1.2. For soils which can be sieved in the field, θ_f (field moisture content of the fine earth) is converted to θ_{vf} (volumetric moisture content) and, using the stone content (V_s), expressed as % of the whole soil. For soils which cannot be sieved in the field, θ_{vt} must be calculated from the field mass of soil and stones (M) minus oven dry weight (M_d). For very large samples M_d may be estimated by air drying the whole soil, and deducting an end-correction obtained by oven drying a representative 0·5 kg sample of fine earth and a separate sample of stone if the stones are porous.

In the absence of an undisturbed core, a field capacity measurement, air capacity (at field capacity) and water content at 15 bars are all that can usefully be quoted for stony soils. A prepared core of sieved fine earth can be tested for water content at intermediate suctions, but the results should be accepted only with reservation, as their significance depends on achieving a bulk density similar to the original field state.

5 Mineralogical Analyses

P. Bullock and P. J. Loveland

5.1 PRETREATMENT AND FRACTIONATION

The mineralogy of the clay fraction and of fractions coarser than clay are conveniently assessed separately, following pretreatment and separation of the fractions using the methods of particle-size analysis. Preparatory treatments, including removal of carbonates, organic matter and iron oxides, depend on the nature of the sample and the objective of the analysis. Because pretreatments can alter or dissolve clay-size minerals, only those needed to disperse and separate the clay and prepare it for instrumental or chemical analysis are generally applied.

Analytical grade reagents are used throughout unless otherwise stated.

5.1.1 Carbonate removal

Reagent

NaOAc/HOAc buffer solution, pH 5: Weigh out 205 g NaOAc. $3H_2O$, add 67 ml HOAc and make up to 2·5 litres with distilled water.

Procedure

Weigh out an amount of air-dry < 2 mm soil which when separated will provide sufficient of each fraction for the mineralogical analyses required. The following quantities of reagent are based on an initial sample of 10 g.

Place the sample in a 250 ml polypropylene centrifuge bottle. Add 120 ml NaOAc/HOAc buffer and leave to stand until most effervescence has ceased. Shake on reciprocating shaker for 1 hour. Centrifuge and pour off *clear* supernatant.

If supernatant is cloudy add a few drops of 0·5M $MgCl_2$ and centrifuge again. When supernatant is clear pour off.

5.1.2 Organic matter removal

Reagent

H_2O_2 27–30% (S.L.R.) (100 vol.): Dilute to 40 vol.

Procedure

To the decarbonated sample (or to the original sample if the soil is non-calcareous) add 50 ml 40 vol. H_2O_2. Cover with watch glass and leave overnight. (If frothing is excessive add a few drops of octan-2-ol.) Heat

on steam bath for 3–4 hours and allow to cool. If organic matter clearly remains, repeat peroxidation.
Note: An explosion may result if samples are allowed to dry on the steam bath.

5.1.3 Iron oxide removal

Reagents

$Na_3C_6H_5O_7$ (sodium citrate), 0·3M
$NaHCO_3$, M
$Na_2S_2O_4$, powder (S.L.R.)

Procedure

Add 5 ml M $NaHCO_3$ and 40 ml 0·3M $Na_3C_6H_5O_7$ to sample in 100 ml polypropylene centrifuge tube. Warm to 80°C (but not above) in water-bath and add 1 g of solid $Na_2S_2O_4$ (0·5 g for clays with little free iron oxide). Stir constantly for 1 minute and at intervals during next 15 minutes. Centrifuge at 3,000 rpm for 10 minutes. If Si, Al and/or Fe determinations in the extract are to be made, decant supernatant into volumetric flask. Repeat treatment if ferruginous colouration remains.

Reference

Mehra, O. P. and Jackson, M. L. (1960). Iron oxide removal from soils and clays by a dithionite-citrate system buffered with sodium bicarbonate. *Clays Clay Miner.* **5,** 317–27.

5.1.4 Clay separation

Apparatus

Shaking machine, end-over-end
Vacuum pump
Freeze drier
Litre measuring cylinders
Centrifuge (M.S.E. Medium, Appendix, p. 82)
Plunger, brass rod fitted with a perforated rubber bung slightly smaller in diameter than the measuring cylinders
Siphoning tube: borosilicate tube (6 mm i.d.) fitted with 60 cm length of polythene tubing

Reagents

5% Calgon: Dissolve 50 g sodium hexametaphosphate (Calgon flake, S.L.R.) and 7 g Na_2CO_3 (anhydrous) in water and dilute to 1 litre.
0·5M $MgCl_2$: Dissolve 51 g $MgCl_2.6H_2O$ in water and dilute to 500 ml.

Procedure

Transfer pretreated soil (using approx. 250 ml water) to a 500 ml bottle containing 10 ml 5% Calgon. Shake overnight on end-over-end shaker. Transfer to a 1 litre measuring cylinder and make up to 1 litre. When equilibrium temperature is reached, stir vigorously with the plunger for 1 minute and allow to sediment. The time needed for sedimentation of the 2 μm fraction for a particular siphoning depth and temperature can be calculated from Table 4, Section 3.2.1, or by reference to Tanner and Jackson (1947). After the appropriate time siphon off into a 3 litre beaker, taking care to wash any residue in the siphoning tube into the beaker. Repeat siphoning five times.

Flocculate clay by adding 2 ml 0·5M $MgCl_2$ after each siphoning.

Siphon off the clear supernatant from the 3 litre beaker using a vacuum pump, and transfer the clay suspension to a 250 ml centrifuge bottle. Centrifuge at 3000 rpm on M.S.E. medium centrifuge for 15 minutes or until supernatant clears, and siphon off supernatant. Add 50 ml water to the centrifuge bottle and mix the residue thoroughly using a perspex rod, taking care to wash any residue on the rod into the bottle. Refill bottle with water and repeat centrifugation. Remove supernatant and freeze dry residue. Transfer the dried clay to a vial and label.

Reference

TANNER, C. B. and JACKSON, M. L. (1947). Nomographs of sedimentation times for soil particles under gravity or centrifugal acceleration. *Proc. Soil Sci. Soc. Am.* **12,** 60–5.

5.1.5 Separation of sand and silt fractions

Apparatus

Sieves—63 μm (4ϕ); 212 μm (2·25ϕ); 600 μm (0·75ϕ)
Sieve shaking machine
Clock

Procedure

The sand fraction is separated from the silt fraction by wet sieving. Place a 63 μm sieve on top of funnel over a 600 ml beaker. Transfer clay-free residue (Section 5.1.4) from centrifuge bottle to sieve using a wash bottle. Agitate sieve contents gently with rubber policeman and jets of water until the washing solution coming through sieve and funnel is clear. Place sieve on watchglass and dry in oven at 105°C. When dry transfer sand from sieve and any which has passed through to the watchglass on drying to a labelled vial.

The sand is further fractionated by transferring it to the topmost sieve, normally 600 or 212 μm, with lid and receiver, and placing on the sieve shaking machine for 15 min. The sand fraction retained on each sieve is transferred to a labelled vial. Particles in the receiver should be added to the silt fraction.

To obtain total silt, pour off clear supernatant from the suspension in the 600 ml beaker, and dry beaker and residue in oven at 105°C. When dry transfer silt to labelled vial.

To fractionate silt, mark the beaker at 10 cm from inside bottom, fill to mark with water, take temperature and after the appropriate settling time (Table 6) decant supernatant into another vessel. Repeat several times until supernatant is clear.

Oven dry residue after final decantation and transfer to labelled vial.

TABLE 6

Times of Gravity Sedimentation of Silt Particles

(sp. gr. 2·65, 10 cm suspension depth)

Particle limiting diameter	*Time required for sedimentation at a suspension temperature of*			
	20°C		*25°C*	
μm	*min*	*s*	*min*	*s*
60		31		27
20	4	40	4	10
6	50		45	

5.1.6 Fractionation of sand and silt separates

Apparatus (Apppendix, p. 82)

Dawe 300/150 watt Soniclean generator
Dawe Ultrasonic Cleaning Tank
600 ml tall-form Pyrex beakers
M.S.E. Medium centrifuge with swing-out head
M.S.E. 50 ml conical H.R. glass centrifuge tubes with rubber caps
Separating funnels

Materials

Bromoform (sp. gr. 2.89)
Acetone S.L.R.
HCl 1M

Procedure

If grain coatings have not been removed already (Sections 5.1.1–

5.1.5), the particle-size separate is placed in a 600 ml beaker with at least 250 ml distilled water, and agitated ultrasonically for 10 minutes. This is repeated until microscopic examination shows the grains are clean enough. If ultrasonic cleaning is insufficient the dithionite-citrate-bicarbonate procedure (Section 5.1.3) is used. In extreme cases (*e.g.* iron pans) the grains are washed in warm 1M HCl, but this removes acid-soluble minerals such as carbonates and phosphates.

To fractionate *sand* sized grains, set up the separating funnel in a fume cupboard and beneath it place a filter paper in a funnel. Place another funnel lined with filter paper alongside and a beaker beneath each funnel. Half fill the separating funnel with bromoform, pour in the weighed dry sample (up to 15 g), pour in more bromoform, stir vigorously, and leave for 15 minutes. Dislodge grains which adhere to the sides by gentle tapping. When light and heavy fractions are clearly separated, allow the heavy minerals to fall onto the filter paper. Close the tap before any light minerals pass through, then allow the light fraction to fall onto the other filter paper. Place both funnels over a large beaker and wash the fractions on the filter papers thoroughly with acetone. Dry thoroughly, brush the separates into weighed vials, and reweigh to calculate proportions of light and heavy fractions.

To fractionate *silt* sized grains (> 20 μm), half fill a conical glass centrifuge tube with bromoform, add 1–2 g weighed dry silt and stir thoroughly. Cap the tube and centrifuge at 1500 rpm for 10 minutes, making sure the tube is well cushioned against breakage. Line two funnels with filter paper. Place the bottom end of the centrifuge tube in a salt/ice mixture. Entrap the heavy minerals by allowing a sufficient depth of bromoform to freeze. Quickly pour off the unfrozen bromoform containing the light fraction onto a filter paper, washing any remaining light minerals out of the tube with bromoform. Empty the frozen bromoform containing the heavy fraction onto a second filter paper and allow to melt. Place both filter papers in funnels over a large beaker and proceed as for sand sized material.

Note: Bromoform is toxic and carcinogenic. Avoid breathing vapour and prevent contact with eyes or skin. Avoid contamination of bromoform with acetone so that it can be re-used.

5.2 CLAY MINERALOGY

Soil clays, separated after removal of carbonates (if present), organic matter and iron oxides, consist largely of crystalline layer-lattice minerals, *e.g.* kaolinite, mica (illite), montmorillonite, vermiculite and chlorite, with variable but usually small amounts of amorphous aluminosilicates and oxides or hydroxides not removed by citrate-dithionite treatment. The crystalline minerals in the separate are identified by X-ray diffraction.

This is used in conjunction with other determinations, including cation exchange capacity (Section 3.3.7) and non-exchangeable potassium content (Section 5.2.1) to obtain semi-quantitative estimates of the proportions of different clay mineral groups.

5.2.1 Non-exchangeable potassium

Apparatus

EEL flame photometer
Platinum crucibles (30 ml capacity)
Sand bath

Reagents

40% HF
Concentrated H_2SO_4 (sp. gr. about 1·84)
K standard: Dissolve 0·1907 g KCl in distilled water and dilute to 100 ml giving 1000 μg K/ml. Dilute × 100 to give a working standard of 10 μg K/ml.

Procedure

Weigh exactly 0·05 g of oven-dry Mg-saturated sample into a platinum crucible. Moisten with a few drops of distilled water, add about 2 ml 40% HF and, cautiously, about 4 ml concentrated H_2SO_4. Heat on the sand bath until dense white fumes appear. Remove from heat, allow to cool and add about 2 ml distilled water. Reheat until fumes appear. Remove, allow to cool, add about 5 ml distilled water and warm briefly. Transfer the crucible contents quantitatively to a 200 ml graduated flask containing about 100 ml distilled water and dilute to volume. Set the flame photometer such that full scale deflection is obtained by the 10 μg K/ml standard. Measure the scale deflection of the unknown. The maximum potassium content measurable at this dilution is 4%.

Calibration

Construct a calibration graph of scale deflection versus μg K/ml using suitably diluted aliquots of the 10 μg K/ml standard.

Calculation

Obtain the potassium content as μg K/ml from the calibration graph, then:

$$\%\ K_2O = (\mu g\ K/ml) \times 0{\cdot}482.$$

References

DEAN, J. A. (1960). *Flame photometry*. McGraw-Hill, London, p. 170.

PRUDEN, G. and KING, H. G. C. (1969). A scheme of semi-micro analysis for the major elements in clay minerals, based on modifications to conventional methods of silicate analysis. *Clay Minerals*, **8**, 1–13.

5.2.2 Preparation of slides for X-ray diffraction

Apparatus (Appendix, p. 82)

High-speed mixer mill
Polystyrene mixing vial with polyethylene cap
Methacrylate balls to fit into vials
Ultrasonic probe
Furnace
Capillary pipette
Glass X-ray slides
Philips X-ray diffractometer and heated stage
Desiccators

Materials

HCl
Ethylene glycol
$CaCl_2$ (technical)

Procedure

Lightly crush the freeze-dried clay and transfer to a glass vial. Weigh out 0·14 g clay into the polystyrene mixing vial containing a methacrylate ball. Fill with distilled water and shake on high speed mixer mill for 2 minutes. Complete dispersion using an ultrasonic probe for 20 s.

Using a capillary pipette, siphon off a small amount of dispersed clay from the vial and spread across an X-ray slide, previously cleaned in conc. HCl. Take the clay suspension completely to the edges of the slide but do not allow to run over. Allow to air dry overnight.

Four slides (a–d) are prepared of each sample as follows. If both kaolinite and chlorite are thought to be present a further subsample should be digested in 50% HCl for 15 minutes at 100°C to remove chlorite, washed and prepared as an additional slide (e).

Slides:

(a) Air-dried, no further treatment.
(b) Place air-dried slide in a desiccator containing ethylene glycol, and transfer desiccator to oven set at 80°C for 4 hours.
(c) Heat in furnace at 335° for 4 hours and store in desiccator containing dried $CaCl_2$ until examined by X-ray diffraction.
(d) Heat in furnace at 550°C for 4 hours and store in desiccator containing dried $CaCl_2$ until examined by X-ray diffraction.
(e) HCl treated sample.

Each of the slides is examined by X-ray diffraction, (c) and (d) being placed on a heated stage at approximately 120°C instead of a normal stage.

5.2.3 Identification of clay minerals

The mineral species present are identified by observing and comparing spacing and intensity of peaks in diffractometer traces obtained from samples treated as described above (Table 7). Most soil clays contain a mixture of clay minerals and many show some degree of interstratification.

Smectite is distinguished from vermiculite and chlorite by treatment with ethylene glycol, which increases the interplanar spacing given by the former to 17 Å + while those given by the latter two remain at 14 Å.

Vermiculite and smectite collapse to 10 Å spacings on heating to 335°C, thus enhancing the mica peaks, provided that there is no hydroxy-aluminium or iron deposited between layers. If these interlayer cations are present, collapse on heating is incomplete and either a shoulder on the 10 Å peak or peaks between 10 Å and 12 Å appear.

Kaolinite peaks disappear on heating to 550°C and at this temperature there are changes in the chlorite structure, causing strengthening of the first order 14 Å reflection and weakening of the 2nd, 3rd and 4th order reflections.

Clays containing interstratified layers characteristic of different minerals commonly occur in soils. Interstratification may be regular, in which case the diffraction peaks represent the sum of the layer thicknesses of component minerals, or it may be random. Diffraction maxima for randomly interstratified clay minerals are commonly found at positions intermediate between those characteristic of the components. With soil clays, usually only the first order peak is strong enough to be observed. It occurs at the position representing the mean of the thickness of the component layers weighted according to their relative proportions. For example, a randomly interstratified mineral containing 80% of 14 Å layers and 20% of 10 Å layers would show a maximum at about $14{\cdot}0 \times 0{\cdot}8 + 10 \times 0{\cdot}2 = 13{\cdot}2$ Å.

Accessory minerals in the clay fraction *e.g.* quartz, feldspars, iron oxides (if not removed by pretreatment) can also be recognized by X-ray diffraction, as many give strong characteristic reflections (Jackson 1964).

Reference

JACKSON, M. L. (1964) Soil clay mineralogical analysis. In: *Soil Clay Mineralogy* (Ed. C. I. Rich and G. W. Kunze), pp. 245–94. Univ. of North Carolina Press.

5.2.4 Semi-quantitative estimation of crystalline clay minerals

Clay minerals cannot be determined quantitatively by comparison of intensities of peak areas on diffractometer traces because individual minerals differ in mass absorption coefficient, orientation of grains, crystal

TABLE 7
Standard Diffraction Spacings (Å) and Strength of Reflections
(Mg-saturated clay)

Mineral group	*Treatment (b) Ethylene glycol*	*Treatment (c) 335°C heating*	*Treatment (d) 550°C heating*
Kaolinite	7·1–7·3 strong 3·57 strong	Same as (b) but may lose some intensity	No peaks
Mica	10·0–10·2 very strong 5·0–5·1 strong (muscovite) 5·0–5·1 weak (biotite) 3·34 very strong	Same as (b) (collapse of expansible minerals enhances 10 Å)	Same as (b)
Halloysite	10·1–10·7	7·2–7·4	No peaks
Vermiculite	14·0–14·2 very strong 7·0–7·1 weak-strong 4·67+ medium 3·50+ medium	No 14 Å left, all to 10 Å	Same as 335°C
Smectite	17·7 very strong 8·9 weak 5·9 very weak 4·5–4·6 strong 3·5+ weak	No spacings greater than 10 Å	Same as 335°C
Chlorite	14·0–14·3 weak-strong 7·0–7·1 very strong 4·7–4·8 medium strong 3·5–3·6 very strong	Same as (b) but may lose some intensity	14·0–14·3 very strong 7·0–7·1 absent or very weak 4·7–4·8 absent or very weak

perfection and chemical constitution. At most a semi-quantitative estimate of proportions of different crystalline clay-mineral groups can be made from peak areas, peak intensities or comparison with a mineral added to the sample in a known proportion to act as an internal standard. Chemical and physical analyses are used to supplement diffraction data.

The relative proportions of expansible mineral and mica (including illite) groups are obtained by comparing the 10 Å reflection of a glycollated sample with that after heating to 335°C and dividing the difference in area beneath the two peaks by a factor of two. Relative peaks show which expansible minerals are present. Non-exchangeable K_2O values (Section 5.2.1) give an approximate indication of the amount of mica present on the basis that soil-clay mica contains around 8% K_2O.

Kaolinite and chlorite are weighted in relation to mica by dividing their peak areas by 3 and 2 respectively, and to distinguish between kaolinite and chlorite when both are present the diffraction pattern of the hydrochloric acid treated sample is compared with patterns a–d (Section 5.2.3).

Although components present in interstratified minerals can be recognized by their behaviour on glycollation and heating in the same way as individual minerals, it is difficult to determine the proportions of each component without detailed research. An approximation can be obtained by taking the position of the first peak to represent the mean of the thickness of the component layers weighted according to their relative proportions. The relative proportions of interstratified minerals are then determined in the same way as for individual mineral groups.

Cation exchange capacity (Section 3.3.7) values are used to supplement X-ray diffraction data. The following clay mineralogical classes are recognized on this basis.

Kaolinitic: clays with $< 3{\cdot}5\%$ K_2O, C.E.C. < 30 me/100 g, and more kaolinite than any other identifiable mineral group.
Smectite: other clays with C.E.C. $\geqslant 45$ me/100 g and more smectite than vermiculite.
Vermiculite: other clays with C.E.C. $\geqslant 45$ me/100 g and more vermiculite than smectite.
Micaceous: other clays with $\geqslant 3{\cdot}5\%$ K_2O.
Chloritic: other clays, with more chlorite than any other identifiable mineral group.
Mixed: other clays.

These classes are applicable to clays in which iron and aluminium oxides occur only as subordinate components and in which the cation exchange capacity is primarily attributable to layer lattice minerals.

5.3 MINERALOGY OF SILT AND SAND FRACTIONS

Minerals of coarse silt (20–60 μm) size and larger are identified using a standard petrographic microscope, and their proportions estimated by grain counts. For most purposes, such as checking lithological discontinuities in profiles or estimating proportions of weatherable silicate minerals, it is preferable to study the fraction that constitutes the greatest proportion of the soil.

5.3.1 Mounting the sample

Apparatus

Hotplate
Microscope slides 7·5 × 2·5 cm
Cover slips

Materials

Clove oil
Canada balsam
Piperine
Xylene

Procedure

Temporary mounts of light minerals can be made, using clove oil ($n = 1{\cdot}53$) as a medium. Place a small amount of the oil on a microscope slide and allow it to spread to the desired area. Sprinkle sufficient sample uniformly over the oil and cover by gently lowering a cover slip onto the sample.

For heavy minerals, piperine with a higher refractive index ($n = 1{\cdot}68$), is used. To avoid crystallization of piperine after a few days, boil for 1 hour at 180°C before applying it, still melted, to the glass slide. Sample and cover slip are applied as for the clove oil preparation of light minerals.

Canada balsam ($n = 1{\cdot}54$) is the most commonly used medium for permanent mounting of light minerals. The balsam is spread over the desired area of the slide, grains sprinkled onto it and the cover slip added. When the balsam has set, any extruding beneath the cover glass can be removed with a scalpel and the slide cleaned with xylene. The slide should then be labelled with relevant details. Piperine is used instead of Canad balsam for permanent mounts of heavy minerals.

5.3.2 Mineral identification and analysis

Apparatus

Petrological microscope
Quartz wedge
Gypsum and mica plates
Refractive index oils (Appendix, p. 82)
Mounted needle
Tweezers
Point counter

Procedure

For identification, a set of tables for the systematic determination of minerals from their optical constants (*e.g.* Larsen and Berman 1964) and/or from their physical and chemical properties (*e.g.* Jones and Fleming 1965) is needed.

The slide should first be scanned under low magnification ($\times$ 10 to

× 32) to become familiar with the grain assemblage. This should be followed by a systematic investigation of the minerals present using the system outlined below:

Crossed nicols, transmitted light, low–high magnification

(i) Isotropism or anisotropism
(ii) Extinction, including angle where relevant
(iii) Birefringence
(iv) Interference colours
(v) Relative retardation and vibration directions
(vi) Twinning

Plane polarized transmitted light, low–high magnification

(i) Colour
(ii) Pleochroism
(iii) Refractive index compared with embedding medium
(iv) Habit
(v) Cleavage
(vi) Parting
(vii) Fracture
(viii) Inclusions

Crossed nicols, convergent light, Bertrand lens, high magnification

(i) Interference figures
(ii) Optic sign of crystal using quartz wedge or gypsum or mica plate
(iii) Optic axial angle
(iv) Dispersion of optic axes

During the examination of a slide, mineral grains difficult to identify without refined tests can be taken from the slide if it is a temporary mount with mounted needle and tweezers. The grain can then be subjected to various tests, one of the most valuable being the determination of precise refractive index by the immersion method. The given mineral is immersed in a drop of selected refractive index liquid on a glass slide and its relative relief observed. By applying the Becke test it is possible to determine whether the mineral has a higher or lower index than the immersing medium. The mineral is then transferred to other oils of known refractive index until the indices of the mineral and medium are the same as shown by the grain appearing almost invisible.

Minerals modified by weathering and aggregates of grains are common in soils. The alteration products and type of aggregation should be described.

Estimates of the abundance of particular minerals and aggregates can be made by counting on arbitrary, regularly spaced traverses. The number of grains which should be counted depends on the accuracy required. Counting 500 grains is usually sufficient to give a good idea of the composition. A point counter facilitates this work (Section 6.2.1).

References

JONES, M. P. and FLEMING, M. G. (1965). *Identification of mineral grains*. Elsevier.
LARSEN, E. S. and BERMAN, H. (1964). *The microscopic determination of the nonopaque minerals*. Bull. U.S. geol. Surv. 848.

6 Micromorphology

P. Bullock

Thin sections are useful in the study of soil microstructure, in elucidating pedologic processes and in soil classification. They enable the soil to be studied microscopically in a relatively undisturbed state and offer a means of extending the description of soils to include characteristics that cannot otherwise be determined.

Aggregates, concretions, nodules, secondary pseudomorphs and weathered grains are best studied in thin section. Sand and silt grains can also be identified mineralogically, although only crude measurements of refractive indices can be made by comparison with the known refractive index of the embedding medium. Clay translocation and weathering are among important pedologic processes that can be studied, micromorphology affording the principal means by which illuvial clay in soil horizons is identified. The size, shape and arrangement of soil constituents and voids revealed in thin sections are also significant in soil-plant relationships.

6.1 DESCRIPTION OF THIN SECTIONS

Before attempting to describe a thin section in detail, it is desirable to gain an overall appreciation of the features in the section and, where possible, to compare it with sections from neighbouring horizons. This cursory examination is made at various magnifications ($\times$ 10 to $\times$ 500) with various degrees of illumination, both in plane polarized light and between crossed nicols.

Particular features of the section should then be described systematically. These are briefly defined below, using the concepts and terms introduced by Brewer (1964) with minor modifications.

The proportionate areas of particular features, *e.g.* argillans, voids, can be estimated by point count measurements (Sections 6.2.1). Micromorphologically, soil material is considered to consist of two groups of solid constituents termed skeleton and plasma; the *skeleton* includes individual mineral grains and organic fragments of silt size and coarser, that are not readily translocated, concentrated or re-organized by pedologic processes; *plasma* is that part of a soil material, usually comprising clay minerals, sesquioxides or organic matter, capable of being moved or having been moved, re-organized or concentrated by pedologic processes. The spatial arrangement of skeleton, plasma and voids is termed *soil fabric.*

Reference

Brewer, R. (1964). *Fabric and mineral analysis of soils.* Wiley, New York.

6.1.1 Related distribution patterns

In describing a soil fabric, two aspects are considered—the orientation pattern and the distribution pattern, each being divided into three classes basic, referred and related. The basic pattern refers to the orientation or distribution of like individuals (*e.g.* clay particles) with regard to each other; the referred pattern to the orientation or distribution of like individuals with regard to a specific reference feature; and the related pattern to the orientation or distribution of like individuals with regard to individuals of a different kind.

Specific names have been given to certain related distribution patterns, as follows.

Porphyroskelic: the plasma occurs as a dense groundmass in which skeleton grains are set after the manner of phenocrysts in a porphyritic rock.

Agglomeroplasmic: the plasma occurs as loose or incomplete fillings in the intergranular spaces between skeleton grains.

Intertextic: skeleton grains are linked by intergranular braces or are embedded in a porous groundmass.

Granular: there is no plasma, or all the plasma occurs as pedological features (see below).

6.1.2 Skeleton grains

These include mineral grains and resistant siliceous and organic bodies larger than about 20 μm. Important characteristics of skeleton grains include *size, distribution* (*i.e.* uniform or non-uniform), *mineralogy* (including degree of weathering), degree of *rounding* and *sphericity.*

6.1.3 Voids

Voids are classified according to their morphology and related and referred distribution patterns as follows:

Simple packing voids: voids resulting from random packing of single grains (*e.g.* in granular fabric).

Compound packing voids: voids resulting from the packing of compound individuals, *e.g.* peds (see below), which do not accommodate each other.

Vughs: relatively large voids, other than packing voids, usually irregular and not normally interconnected with other voids of comparable size.

Vesicles: voids whose walls consist of smooth, simple curves.

Channels: voids, larger than those resulting from normal packing, with a cylindrical form. Branching patterns can be single, dendroid, anastomosing or trellised.

Chambers: unlike vughs in that their walls are regular and smoothed, and unlike vesicles and vughs in that they are interconnected through channels.

Planes: voids that are planar according to the ratios of their principal axes. Three types are recognized:

Joint planes: planar voids with a fairly regular pattern, such as parallel and sub-parallel sets.
Skew planes: planar voids which traverse the soil material in an irregular manner.
Craze planes: essentially planar voids with complex conformation of the walls due to the interconnection of many flat or curved planes.

As well as listing the proportions of the various types of voids in a thin section, details should be given of size, shape and arrangement.

Size: according to Jongerius (1957): micropores ($< 30\ \mu m$); mesopores (30–$100\ \mu m$); and macropores ($> 100\ \mu m$).

Shape: conformation (curved, regular or irregular) and smoothness; *ortho* due to random packing of the plasma and skeleton grains, and *meta* with walls smoother than would result from normal packing of plasma and skeleton grains.

Arrangement: intrapedal, interpedal and transpedal.

Reference

JONGERIUS, A. (1957). *Morfologische onderzoekingen over de Bodemstructuur,* Bodenkundige Studies No. 2. Mededelingen van de Stichting voor bodemkartering. Wageningen.

6.1.4 Peds

The structural organization of a soil material is expressed by the development of three units of organization, peds, pedological features and *s*-matrices. A ped is defined as an individual, natural, relatively permanent aggregate separated from others by voids or natural surfaces of weakness.

The basic unit of description is the primary ped. A complete assessment of pedality is often difficult in thin section because the size of units often exceeds the microscopic field even at lowest magnification. However, the *size*, *shape* and *arrangement* of primary peds and the extent of formation of secondary and tertiary peds should be recorded where possible.

6.1.5 Pedological features

These are recognizable units within a soil material which are distinguished from enclosing material for any reason such as origin, differences in concentration of some fraction of the plasma or differences in arrangement of the constituents.

They can be distinguished according to their pattern of occurrence in relation to peds as intrapedal, interpedal, or transpedal, and classified into the following morphological groups.

1. ***Cutans*** are modifications in composition or arrangement of constituents at natural surfaces in soil materials. They may result from *absolute concentration* of particular plasma constituents, *e.g.* clay minerals, sesquioxides; from *relative concentration* of coarser constituents, *i.e.* skeleton grains by removal of plasmic material; or from *in situ modification* of the soil at the interface (plasma separation), *e.g.* preferred orientation caused by stress.

They are classified according to the surface with which they are associated, *e.g. ped*, *free grain*, *embedded grain*, *normal void*, *channel* and *plane* cutans.

They can also be characterized according to the nature of the cutanic material, *e.g. argillans*, *sesquans*, *mangans*, *soluans* (*e.g.* of alkaline earth carbonates or more soluble salts), *silans* (silica) and *skeletans* (skeleton grains adhering to the surface), resulting from either absolute or relative concentration.

Quasicutans are obviously related to natural surfaces but do not immediately adjoin them.

They are described using the same terminology as for cutans.

2. ***Pedotubules*** are features consisting of soil material (skeleton grains or skeleton grains plus plasma) with tubular external form and relatively sharp boundaries.

They are distinguished by:

(a) *Internal fabric*
Granotubules: composed of skeleton grains without plasma, or all plasma occurs as pedological features (granular fabric).
Aggrotubules: formed of recognizable aggregates showing no directional arrangement with regard to the external form of the pedotubule.
Isotubules: no recognizable aggregates and no directional arrangement with regard to external form (essentially porphyroskelic).
Striotubules: without recognizable aggregates but the basic fabric shows a directional arrangement related to the external form.
(b) *Nature of tubulic material: e.g.* organic, sesquioxidic, siliceous etc.
(c) *External form of tubules*
Cross-sectional shape, *e.g.* circular, elliptical, arched etc. and type of branching, *e.g.* single, dendroid, trellised etc.
(d) *Genetic groups*
Orthotubules: material derived from the horizon in which they occur.
Metatubules: material derived from another horizon.
Paratubules: material unlike that of any horizon in the profile.

3. ***Glaebules*** are 3 dimensional units usually prolate to equant in shape, embedded in the soil matrix. Their morphology (*i.e.* size, shape, internal fabric) is incompatible with formation within a single void in the present soil material. They are recognized as units because of a greater concentration of some constituent and/or a difference in fabric compared with the enclosing soil material, or because they have a distinct boundary with the enclosing material.
The following groups are recognized:

1. *Nodules:* with an undifferentiated internal fabric, including recognizable rock and soil fabrics.
2. *Concretions:* with a generally concentric fabric.
3. *Septaria:* with a series of radiating cracks crossed by cracks concentric with the margin.
4. *Pedodes:* with a hollow interior, often with a drusy lining of crystals.
5. *Glaebular halos:* weak accumulations of some fraction surrounding a much stronger glaebular feature, having an undifferentiated structure and diffuse external boundary.
6. *Papules:* composed of clay minerals with continuous (*i.e.* with extinction characteristics of strong continuous orientation) and/or lamellar fabric (*i.e.* with constituents arranged in parallel planar zones), with sharp external boundaries.

Glaebules are further characterized by:
Internal fabric, e.g. undifferentiated, concentric, lamellar, continuous.

Mineralogical nature, e.g. ferruginuous, manganiferous, carbonate, sulphate, siliceous and argillaceous.
Distinctness, e.g. sharpness of external boundary (sharp to very diffuse) and ease of separation (discrete, weakly to strongly adhesive).
Shape, e.g. amygdaloidal, bladed, boytryoidal, convolute, mamillated and reniform.

4. ***Crystallaria*** are single crystals or arrangements of crystals of relatively pure fractions of the plasma that do not enclose other soil material but form cohesive masses. Their morphology is consistent with their formation in original voids in the enclosing soil material.
They are classified as follows:

(a) *Crystal tubes:* crystallaria that occur in channels of simple or branching acicular shape.
(b) *Crystal chambers:* usually prolate to equant crystallaria formed in vughs, vesicles and chambers.
(c) *Crystal sheets:* planar crystallaria.
(d) *Intercalary crystals:* crystallaria consisting of single large crystals or groups of a few large crystals set in the soil material and apparently unassociated with voids of similar size and shape to the crystallaria as a whole. The crystals are euhedral to subhedral.
Crystallaria may be characterized by:
Internal fabric: according to either preferred orientation of the crystals with regard to the enclosing soil material or the basic orientation of the crystals with regard to each other. These are *parallel*, *normal*, *spherulitic*, *crystallographic* and *random*.
Kind of void: e.g. channels, planes, vughs, vesicles and chambers.
Mineralogical nature.

6.1.6 S-matrices

The *s*-matrix of a soil material is the material within primary peds, or composing apedal soil materials, within which pedological features occur. It consists of *plasma*, *skeleton grains* and *voids*.

The term plasmic fabric refers to the basic arrangement of plasma particles in the matrix with regard to each other and is based on the interpretation of optical properties between crossed nicols, especially extinction phenomena, due to:

1. Visible crystals of plasma;
2. The kind and degree of orientation of the plasma grains, including distinctions between opaque, isotropic and anisotropic plasma;
3. The kind and degree of preferred orientation of domains (Aylmore

and Quirk 1959, Emerson 1959), as evidenced by flecked and striated orientation patterns; and particularly
4. The kind and degree of development of plasma separations.

Plasmic fabrics are classified into five types, *asepic*, *sepic*, *undulic*, *isotic* and *crystic*, on the basis of their general anisotropy and extinction patterns. Each of these groups is subdivided according to details of their extinction pattern. Plasmic materials can also be classified according to the proportion of organic matter they contain (Section 6.1.7). The most usual magnification for viewing plasmic fabrics is × 70 to × 120.

1. ***Asepic plasmic fabric*:** the plasma is dominantly anisotropic, with little organic matter and domains largely unoriented with regard to each other, giving a flecked extinction pattern. There are no well defined plasma separations.

Argillasepic fabric: dominantly of anisotropic clay minerals and exhibits a flecked orientation pattern with recognizable domains.
Silasepic fabric: wide range of particle sizes but with a relatively large proportion of silt-size grains, making domains difficult to recognize.

2. ***Sepic plasmic fabrics*:** the plasma contains little organic matter and shows more or less well defined plasma separations, giving striated extinction patterns.

Insepic fabric: plasma separations occur as isolated patches within a dominantly flecked plasma.
Mosepic fabric: a mosaic of patches with striated orientation but unoriented with respect to each other.
Vosepic fabric: plasma separations are associated with, and dominantly parallel to, voids.
Skelsepic fabric: plasma separations with striated orientation occur subcutanically around skeleton grains.
Masepic fabric: plasma separations occur as zones apparently unassociated with the walls of voids or the surfaces of grains. Where plasma separations occur in two or three sets of subparallel zones, the fabric is termed bimasepic or trimasepic respectively.
Lattisepic fabric: short discontinuous separations occur in a lattice-like pattern.
Omnisepic fabric: all the plasma exhibits a complex striated orientation pattern.

Soil materials often exhibit combinations of the above sepic fabrics. Where several are present, the best developed variant is named last, *e.g.* skel-mo-masepic.

3. ***Undulic plasmic fabric*:** the plasma is practically isotropic at low magnifications and weakly anisotropic with faint undulic extinction at high magnification. It usually contains relatively large amounts of colloidal organic matter, iron oxides, or both. An inundulic fabric is a variety of undulic fabric in which small rather indistinct domains are present.

4. ***Isotic plasmic fabric*:** the plasma is indeterminate even at highest magnifications (*e.g.* $\times$ 500) and highest light intensities.

5. ***Crystic plasmic fabric*:** the plasma is usually anisotropic and consists predominantly of recognizable crystals, usually of the more soluble plasma fractions (*e.g.* calcite, gypsum).

References

AYLMORE, L. A. G. and QUIRK, J. P. (1959). Swelling of clay-water systems. *Nature, Lond.* **183,** 1752–3.
EMERSON, W. W. (1959). The structure of soil crumbs. *J. Soil Sci.* **10,** 235–44.

6.1.7 Organic materials

Kubiena (1953) pioneered the microscopic study of organic remains in soils and in more recent years Jongerius (1962, 1963) and Barratt (1964, 1969) have extended this knowledge. Microscopic definitions of mull, moder, mor and peat and their subdivisions are based on the components of the litter, degree of decomposition, evidence of microfloral and faunal activity, and the occurrence of plasma (normally with an undulic or isotic fabric) in which organic and mineral components are indistinguishable (organo-mineral plasma).

1. ***Components of litter*:** these may be leaves, stems, roots or humified material unrecognizable as to origin. Remains with original structure can be identified by histological techniques.

2. ***Degree of decomposition*:** undecomposed tissues appear more or less entire, showing a cell structure, pale colouration and little or no staining. They are anisotropic and show first order interference colours between crossed nicols.

Little decomposed tissues are stained but cell structure is still apparent. Moderately decomposed tissues are strongly stained, usually brown, and their origin is difficult to recognize because of animal attack and staining. Strongly decomposed tissues are brown to black and their origin is unrecognizable. They are generally fragmented and show little or no birefringence.

3. ***Microfloral and faunal activity*:** microflora are important in the early stages of litter breakdown, causing staining and forming smooth edged cavities in the litter. Coloured mycelia can be identified where present, but staining, *e.g.* with revector soluble blue, is necessary to reveal any white hyphae and bacteria.

The activity of soil fauna is usually indicated by their droppings, and a knowledge of dropping forms permits the recognition of the role of particular faunal groups in the decomposition of organic residues. Although some species may produce more than one type of dropping, depending on the material ingested, four main groups of *faecal pellets* can be recognized according to their origin:

Mites: small (<250 μm, usually <100 μm) spherical or oval pellets, usually orange brown and little humified in upper layers of plant litter (*L* or *F* horizon), and brown to black and more strongly humified in lower layers. No mineral grains are normally included.
Enchytraeids: small (<250 μm) rugose, sub-spherical pellets, slightly humified, forming an intimate mixture of organic matter and fine mineral grains.
Macro-arthropods: large (250 μm–2 mm), often elongate casts visible to the naked eye and consisting of an intimate mixture of well humified organic matter and mineral grains.
Earthworms: large (>1 mm) well humified, spongy aggregates, rich in mineral matter.

4. ***Organo-mineral plasma*:** the degree of association between organic and mineral fractions depends on the degree of humification of plant material. Only when the latter has been humified as in mull is there a strong association between the clay and organic fractions of the plasma.

References

BARRATT, B. C. (1964). A classification of humus forms and micro-fabrics of temperate grasslands. *J. Soil Sci.* **15,** 342–56.

BARRATT, B. C. (1969). A revised classification and nomenclature of microscopic soil materials with particular reference to organic components. *Geoderma,* **2,** 257–71.

JONGERIUS, A. (1962). Recente vorderingen in de micropedologie en haarmogelijkheden. *Landbouwk. Tijdschr.* **74,** 973–99.

JONGERIUS, A. (1963). Optic-volumetric measurements of some humus forms. In: *Soil Organisms.* J. Doeksen and J. van der Drift (eds.), North Holland Publishing Co., Amsterdam.

KUBIENA, W. L. (1953). *The soils of Europe.* Murby, London.

6.2 OPTICAL MEASUREMENT OF PORE SPACE

Examination of thin sections at moderate magnification (*e.g.* × 100) shows pores down to 2 μm in diameter. Unfortunately, whether the section is examined between crossed nicols or in plane polarized light, there is difficulty in distinguishing easily between voids and some mineral grains, thus making quantitative measurements of pore space liable to error. Between crossed nicols, mineral grains at extinction, some organic matter particles and voids all appear black, while in plane polarized light colourless mineral grains and pores both appear white.

Pore space can be measured quantitatively in thin sections by mixing fluorescent dye with the resin before impregnation of the sample and viewing the finished section under ultraviolet light, when the voids fluoresce strongly in contrast to the solid soil constituents.

6.2.1 Using point counts

Apparatus

Fluorescent microscope
Automatic point counter (Appendix, p. 82)

Procedure

Measurement of pores and mineral grains using a point counter has been shown to be accurate and reliable by Chayes and Fairbairn (1951).

To measure pores by this method, three requirements must be met: firstly a source of ultraviolet light and a fluorescent microscope or a petrological microscope with fluorescent attachment; secondly, the microscope must be fitted with a micrometer ocular with cross hairs; and finally a mechanical stage, preferably linked to an automatic point counter, is needed.

In principle, a section is sampled at regular intervals along a series of linear traverses spaced equidistantly over the slide. The sampling point in each case is the intersection of the crosshairs on the ocular.

The automatic point counter consists of an attachable mechanical stage unit linked to an electrical counter unit. The counter unit has 14 separate keys for individual tabulations and thus total pore space as well as the percentage of different types of voids, *e.g.* vughs, channels etc., can be determined each time a section is scanned. When a count is made by depression of one of the 14 keys, the unit automatically progresses the section a given distance along the traverse. The point counter can be set to move at intervals of 50 μm, 100 μm, 166 μm or 333 μm.

When a section has been scanned completely in one direction it is turned through 90° and re-scanned and an average taken of the two sets of results. This minimizes directional bias.

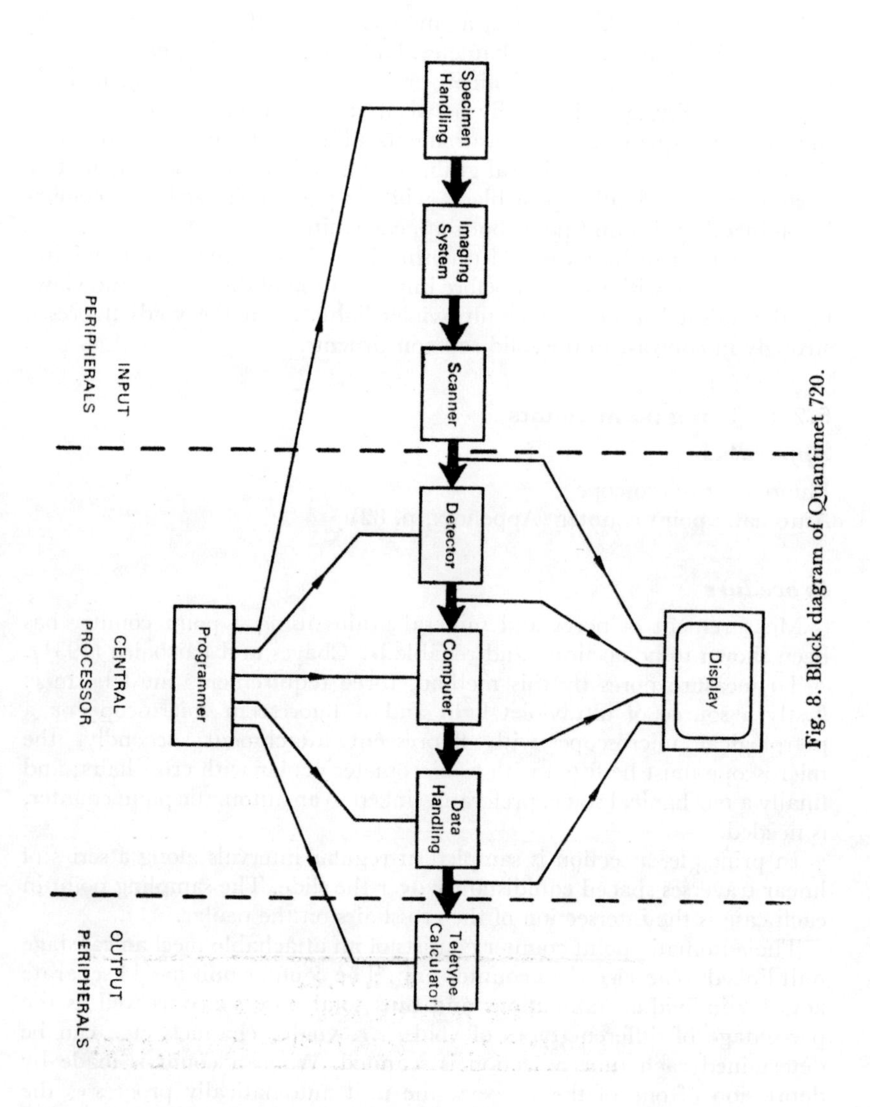

Fig. 8. Block diagram of Quantimet 720.

Accuracy of any analysis using the point counter bears a direct mathematical relationship to the number of points sampled; thus the greater the number of points the more accurate the results. Counting 1500 points gives a probable percentage error of 23 at the 80% confidence interval, so that if the estimated percentage of pores in a section is 10, the true value will be between 7·7 and 12·3 in 4 out of 5 cases.

Reference

Chayes, F. and Fairbairn, H. W. (1951). A test of the precision of thin-section analysis by point counter. *Am. Miner.* **36,** 704–12.

6.2.2 Using quantimet image analyser

Apparatus

Image Analyser with fluorescent microscope

Procedure

Total pore space and pore-size distribution, as well as shape characteristics of pore patterns, can be made more quickly using an image analyser such as Quantimet (Fig. 8).

A section is placed on a fluorescent microscope which acts as the input peripheral, and produces an image which is projected into the scanning system. A vidicon or plumbicon scanner scans this image, and signals from the fluorescing pores are isolated from the rest of the image by a process of 'detection' based on the application of various grey level criteria, *e.g.* all parts lighter or darker than a preset threshold can be detected as can parts between two selected grey levels. The detected signal is then fed into a computer module which makes the measurements, *e.g.* the number of pores, their area, or the number above or below a certain size. Results are shown on the display monitor screen which also shows exactly which features are being measured. Results can also be printed or punched out on paper tape for further processing by a digital computer, or fed directly into a desktop calculator.

APPENDIX

Suppliers of Special Apparatus and Materials

Section 2.1

Rukuhia soil crusher. L. Farnell and Co. Ltd, Potterell's Works, North Mymms, Hatfield, Herts.

Section 2.3.1

Autoplax embedding materials. Automobile Plastics Ltd, 7 Henry Road, New Barnet, Herts.

Uvitex OB fluorescent dye. Ciba-Clayton Ltd, Ullswater Crescent, Coulsdon, Surrey CR3 2HR.

Bakelite resins. B and K Resins Ltd., 130–32 Verdant Lane, London SE6 1LQ.

Section 2.3.2

Carbowax 6000. G. T. Gurr Ltd, P.O. Box 1, Romford RM1 1HA.

Crystal violet dye. Raymond A. Lamb, 6 Sunbeam Road, London NW10 6JL.

Section 2.3.3

Woco 220 diamond saw. Production Techniques Ltd., 11 Tavistock Road, Fleet, Hants.

Dawe ultrasonic cleaner. Dawe Instruments Ltd, Concord Road, Western Avenue, London W3 0SD.

Surface grinding machine. Jones and Shipman Ltd, Narborough Road South, Leicester LE3 2LF.

Universal polisher, *lapping cloths* and *diamond compound*. Metallurgical Services Ltd, Reliant Works, Brockham, Betchworth, Surrey RH3 7AW.

Shell fusus A oil. Gibbs and Dandy Ltd, Chapel Street, Luton, Beds.

Section 3.2.1

Sampling pipette racking stand. Engineering Laboratory Equipment Ltd, Durrants Hill Trading Estate, Apsley, Hemel Hempstead, Herts.

Section 3.5.1

Calcimeter. G. Berneye, 6 Aldwick Road, Harpenden, Herts.

Section 4.1.2

Plastic balls, trade-name 'Allplass'. Capricorn Services Ltd, 49 St James Street, London SW1.

Section 4.2.1

Ground silica flour. British Industrial Sand Ltd, Midland Sales Office, Church Bridge Industrial Estate, Oldbury, Warley, Worcestershire.

Kaolin. English Clays, Lovering and Pochin Co. Ltd, St Austell, Cornwall.

Sections 5.1.4. and 5.1.6.

M.S.E. Medium Centrifuge. Measuring and Scientific Equipment Ltd, 6 Broad Street Place, London EC2M 7JT.

Section 5.1.6

300/150 *watt Soniclean generator*, *Type 1143A*, and *Ultrasonic cleaning tank*, *Type 1165/H45/3*.

Dawe Instruments Ltd., Renault Estate, Western Avenue, London W/3.

Section 5.2.2

High-speed mixer mill, polystyrene mixing vials and *methacrylate balls.* Glen Creston, 37 The Broadway, Stanmore, Middlesex.

Ultrasonic power unit and *probe.* Mullard Equipment Ltd, Mullard House, Torrington Place, London WC1.

Section 5.3.2

Refractive index oils. Rayner and Keeler Ltd, 44 New Cavendish Street, London W1.

Section 6.2.1

Automatic point counter. James Swift and Son Ltd, Joule Road, Houndsmills Industrial Estate, Basingstoke, Hants.

Section 6.2.2

Quantimet Image Analyser. Metals Research Ltd, Melbourn, Cambridgeshire.

[illegible]

[illegible] London
W1

[illegible] James Smith and Sons [illegible]

[illegible]